Acknowledgements

Research contractor	Environmental Protection Group Ltd	
Steering group chairman	Mr Graham Stanley, Taylor Woodrow Construction Ltd	
Funders	Environment Agency	Drinking Water Inspectorate (DWI)
	A Proctor Group	Source Control Systems Ltd
	EPG Ltd	SEL Civil Engineering
	CRM Rainwater Drainage Consultancy	

The research for this publication was commissioned by CIRIA and undertaken by Phil Cooper of EPG Ltd, Steve Wilson of EPG Ltd (formerly of Card Geotechnics Ltd) and Chris Pratt of Coventry University. CIRIA's project managers were Elizabeth Holliday and Daniel J Leggett.

Following established CIRIA practice, the project was guided by a steering group, chaired by Mr Graham Stanley of Taylor Woodrow Construction Ltd and comprising the following members:

Ian Charlton	
Nick Cooper	Alderburgh Ltd
Clive Fisher	Source Control Systems Ltd
Matthew Kean	Environment Agency
Martin Lambley	A Proctor Group
Cliff Nicholls	Transport Research Laboratory
Andrew Shuttleworth	SEL Environmental
Malcolm Wearing	CRM Rainwater Drainage Consultancy Ltd
Peter White	Drinking Water Inspectorate
Peter Wilson	Highways Agency

The project was also guided by the following corresponding steering group members:

Garry Edwards	Entec UK Ltd
Prof Robert Jackson	University of Salford
Bridget Woods-Ballard	HR Wallingford

Acknowledgement is also given to the following for their contribution to the project:

Catherine Abbott	HR Wallingford
Deanne Gibb	Card Geotechnics Limited
Mathew Gilsenan	SEL Environmental
Kirsteen Macdonald	Ewan Associates

The project was funded by the Environment Agency, the Drinking Water Inspectorate (DWI), A Proctor Group, CRM Rainwater Drainage Consultancy, EPG Ltd, SEL Civil Engineering and Source Control Systems Ltd.

CIRIA and the authors gratefully acknowledge the support of these funding organisations and the technical help and advice provided by the members of the steering group. Contributions do not imply that individual funders necessarily endorse all views expressed in published outputs.

Photographs

Figure 2.1 – Steve Wilson

Figure 2.2 – Source Control Systems Limited

Figure 2.3 – Formpave Limited

Figure 2.4 – Steve Wilson

Figure 2.5 – Chris Pratt

Figure 2.6 – Steve Wilson

Figure 2.7 – Chris Pratt

Figure 2.8 – Chris Pratt

CIRIA C582

London 2002

Source control using constructed pervious surfaces

Hydraulic, structural and water quality performance issues

C Pratt

S Wilson

P Cooper

CIRIA *sharing knowledge* ■ *building best practice*

6 Storey's Gate, Westminster, London SW1P 3AU
TELEPHONE 020 7222 8891 FAX 020 7222 1708
EMAIL enquiries@ciria.org.uk
WEBSITE www.ciria.org.uk

Summary

This book discusses the critical issues that should be considered when designing and constructing pervious pavements that are to be used as a technique for stormwater source control. It details the types of surfaces available and provides examples of developments that have used these techniques. The publication discusses issues for consideration relating to the hydraulic, structural and water quality performance of pervious surfaces. Finally, the book provides a design framework, which includes detailed recommendations for methods where necessary.

Source control using constructed pervious surfaces – hydraulic, structural and water quality performance issues

Pratt C, Wilson S, Cooper P

Construction Industry Research and Information Association

CIRIA C582   © CIRIA 2002   RP637   ISBN 0 86017 582 0

British Library Cataloguing in Publication Data
A catalogue record for this book is available from the British Library

Published by CIRIA, 6 Storey's Gate, Westminster, London SW1P 3AU.

Contents

LIST OF FIGURES

LIST OF TABLES

LIST OF BOXES

Glossary

Adsorption – The adherence of gas, vapour or dissolved matter to the surface of solids.

Aquifer – Layer of rock or soil that holds or transmits water.

Asphalt – CEN description of all mixtures of mineral aggregates bound with bituminous materials used in the construction and maintenance of paved surfaces. See Section 1.4.

Asphalt concrete – New CEN description of materials previously known as macadams and Marshall Asphalt. See Section 1.4.

Attenuation – Slowing down the rate of flow to prevent flooding erosion with a consequent increase in the duration of flow.

Base – CEN description of the lowest bound layer of an asphalt pavement known in UK as roadbase. See Section 1.4.

Binder course – CEN description of the second layer of an asphalt pavement known in UK as basecourse. See Section 1.4.

Bitumen – A hydrocarbon binder. A virtually involatile adhesive material derived from crude petroleum that is used to coat mineral aggregate for use in construction and maintenance of paved surfaces.

Block paving – Pre-cast concrete or clay-brick-sized flexible modular paving system.

Boussinesq equation – A method of determining the stress induced at any point within the ground (assumed to be a semi-infinite homogeneous weightless elastic half space) by a load applied vertically to the surface. Developed by a French physicist and mathematician (Boussinesq, 1885).

Capping layer – A layer of unbound aggregate that is of lower quality than sub-base and is used to improve the performance of the foundation soils before laying the sub-base and to protect the subgrade from damage by construction traffic.

Carriageway – That part of the road used to carry vehicular traffic.

Catchment – The area contributing flow to a point on a drainage or river system.

CBR value – California Bearing Ratio; an empirical measure of the stiffness and strength of soils, used in road pavement design.

Construction Quality Assurance (CQA) – A documented management system designed to provide adequate confidence that items or services meet contractual requirements and will perform adequately in service. CQA usually includes inspection and testing of installed components and recording the results.

Continuously graded – A soil or aggregate with a balanced range of particle sizes with significant proportions of all fractions from the maximum nominal size down.

Controlled waters – Waters defined and protected under the Water Resources Act 1991, including inland freshwaters (relevant lakes and ponds, rivers and other watercourses), groundwater and coastal waters. For the full definition refer to the Water Resources Act 1991.

Design criteria – A set of standards agreed by the developer, planners and regulators that the proposed system should satisfy.

Elastic modulus – Also known as Young's Modulus or stiffness modulus; the ratio of stress divided by strain for a particular material.

Fines – Small soil particles less than 63 micron in size.

First flush – Pollutants collect on carriageway and hard surfaces in dry periods. The majority of these are believed to be washed off during the first part of a storm, known as the "first flush". The profile of the pollutants in the runoff is believed also to be dependent on the storm intensity. The profile of the delivery of the pollutants into the drainage system will depend on the relative times of concentration of the various parts of the catchment.

Floodplain – All land adjacent to a watercourse, over which water flows in times of flood (see Environment Agency's *Policy and practice for the protection of flood plains* for a fuller definition).

Footway – Area for pedestrians at the side of the carriageway.

Geocellular structure – A plastic box structure used in the ground.

Geogrid – Plastic grid structure used to increase strength of soils or aggregates.

Geomembrane – An impermeable plastic sheet, typically manufactured from polypropylene, high-density polyethylene or other geosynthetic material.

Geotextile – A plastic fabric which is permeable.

Groundwater Protection Zone (Source Protection Zone) – Area around public water supply borehole where groundwater must be protected from pollution. It is defined by reference to travel times of pollutants within the groundwater. See the Environment Agency's *Policy and practice for the protection of groundwater* for specific details.

Gully – Opening in the road pavement that allows water to enter conventional drainage systems, usually covered by a metal grate.

Hydrograph – A graph showing changes in the rate of flow from a catchment with time.

Impermeable – Will not allow water to pass through it.

Infiltration – The passage of water through a surface, either the pervious surface or into the underlying ground.

Initial rainfall loss – The amount of rain that falls on a surface before water begins to flow off the surface.

Pavement, flexible – A pavement that behaves as a flexible mat under loads, for example asphalt or block paving.

Pavement, rigid – A pavement that acts as a rigid structure under loads, such as concrete slabs.

Percentage runoff – The proportion of rainfall that runs off a surface. See also **runoff**.

Permeability – A measure of the ease with which a fluid can flow through a porous medium. It depends on the physical properties of the medium, for example grain size, porosity and pore shape.

Permeable surface – A surface formed of material that is itself impervious to water but, by virtue of voids formed through the surface, allows infiltration through the pattern of voids, for example concrete block paving.

Pervious surface – A surface that allows inflow of rainwater into the underlying construction or soil.

Poisson's ratio – If an elastic material is subject to compression or tension the cross-sectional area will change as load is applied. Assuming axes are x, y and z, then if the load is applied along the x axis, the strain in the y and z direction is proportional to that in the x direction, but opposite in sign. The constant of proportionality is known as Poisson's ratio.

Porosity – The percentage of the bulk volume of a rock or soil that is occupied by voids, whether isolated or connected.

Porous asphalt – An asphalt material used to make pavement layers pervious, with open voids to allow water to pass through (previously known as pervious macadam).

Porous surface – A surface that infiltrates water across the entire surface of the material forming the surface, such as grass and gravel surfaces, porous concrete and porous asphalt.

Return period – The frequency with which an event occurs. A 100-year storm is one that occurs on average once every 100 years; ie its annual probability of exceedance is 1 per cent (1/100). A 500-year storm is the storm expected to occur once every 500 years, and so has an annual probability of exceedance of 0.2 (1/500).

Road pavement – The load-bearing structure of a road. (Note: the path at the side of a road, commonly referred to as a pavement, is the footway.)

Runoff – Water flow over the ground surface to the drainage system. This occurs if the ground is impermeable or is saturated.

Runoff coefficient – A measure of the amount of rainfall that is converted to runoff.

Single-size grading (single-size material) – The majority of the soil or aggregate particles are of one nominal size, although there may be small proportions of other sizes.

Soakaway – A subsurface structure into which water is conveyed to allow infiltration into the ground.

Source control – The control of runoff at or near its source.

Sub-base – The unbound layer of aggregate used immediately below the bound layers. It is laid on the soil (or capping layer) to provide a stable foundation for construction of the road pavement.

Subgrade – The soils onto which the road pavement is constructed.

SUDS – Sustainable urban drainage system: a sequence of management practices and control structures designed to drain surface water in a more sustainable fashion than some conventional techniques (also referred to as sustainable drainage system, SuDS).

Surface course – CEN description of the top layer of an asphalt pavement, known in UK as wearing course.

Time of entry – Time taken for rainwater to reach an inlet into the drainage system after hitting the ground.

Type 1 sub-base – Specification for the most commonly used sub-base material in conventional pavements, from *Specification for Highway Works*.

Void ratio – The ratio of open air space to solid particles in a soil or aggregate.

ABBREVIATIONS

A_d total area to be drained, including any adjacent impermeable area

A_b base area of infiltration system below pervious pavement

A_1 area of adjacent impermeable surface draining onto pervious surface

A_p area of pervious pavement

AASHTO   American Association of State Highway and Transportation Officials

AOS   apparent opening size

ASTM   American Society for Testing of Materials

BSI   British Standards Institution

BRE   Building Research Establishment

C   shape factor

CBM   cement-bound material

CBR   Californian Bearing Ratio

CEN   Comité Europeén de Normalisation (European Committee for Standardisation)

CQA   construction quality assurance

D   rainstorm duration

D_s effective particle size diameter

D_{10} soil particle size such that 10 per cent of the sample consists of particles having a smaller nominal diameter

D_{15} soil particle size such that 15 per cent of the sample consists of particles having a smaller nominal diameter

D_{50} soil particle size such that 50 per cent of the sample consists of particles having a smaller nominal diameter

D_{85} soil particle size such that 85 per cent of the sample consists of particles having a smaller nominal diameter

DBM   dense bitumen macadam

DMRB   *Design Manual for Roads and Bridges* (The Highways Agency, Scottish Executive Development Department, The National Assembly for Wales and The Department for Regional Development Northern Ireland)

e   void ratio of aggregate

E	Young's Modulus
EA	Environment Agency (England and Wales)
FHWA	Federal Highway Administration
G_s	specific gravity of soil or aggregate particles
h	thickness of aggregate or other storage medium below pervious pavement
h_{max}	maximum depth of water that will occur in the storage medium
i	rainfall intensity
k	coefficient of permeability
MSA	motorway service area
MTBE	methyl tert butyl ether
n	porosity of soil or aggregate
O_{95}	apparent opening size
Q	flow through outlet from storage below pavement
q	infiltration coefficient
r	rainfall ratio
SEPA	Scottish Environment Protection Agency
SUDS	sustainable urban drainage systems
TRL	Transport Research Laboratory (formerly Transport and Road Research Laboratory, TRRL, and Road Research Laboratory, RRL)
T	return period for storm event
USEPA	United States Environmental Protection Agency
V	maximum storage volume for water below pervious pavement
γ_d	dry unit weight of soil or aggregate
γ_w	unit weight of water
μ	viscosity
ν	Poisson's ratio

Foreword

This book is intended for use by developers, landscape architects, consulting engineers, local authorities, architects, highway authorities, environmental regulators, planners, sewerage undertakers, contractors and other organisations involved in the provision or maintenance of surface water drainage to new and existing developments. It discusses the critical issues that must be considered when designing and constructing pervious pavements that are to be used as a technique for stormwater source control.

Section 1 (Introduction) introduces the concepts of source control and the use of pervious surfaces to achieve this. It discusses the background to the development of pervious surfaces as a source control technique and identifies the relationship between this book and other publications from CIRIA and other organisations.

Section 2 (Constructed pervious surface drainage systems) identifies the types of pervious surfaces that have been used, both in the UK and abroad, including the layers used to provide storage below the surface. It gives a brief overview of the historical usage of pervious surfaces and identifies the design approaches that are used today.

Section 3 (Hydraulic performance issues) provides detailed information on matters relating to the hydraulic performance of pervious surfaces. This includes the issues to be considered in design, such as estimating rainfall and runoff from adjacent areas, calculating storage volumes and estimating the outflow hydrographs from the systems. It also looks at the long-term maintenance implications for these types of systems.

Section 4 (Structural performance issues) is concerned with the ability of pervious surfaces to carry the required loads from traffic. It looks at the current methods used to design road pavements and identifies the issues that are critical to the design of pervious surfaces. This includes ways of allowing for the use of different materials within the structure, the effects of frost and the effects of water storage on the foundation soils.

Section 5 (Water quality performance issues) deals with quality of water issuing from outlet pipes or infiltrating into the ground from pervious surface systems. It looks at the mechanisms and processes that occur within pervious surfaces to improve water quality. It also identifies the legislation that applies and the issues to be addressed to avoid causing pollution of either surface or groundwater.

Section 6 (Recommended design methodology) summarises the issues discussed and provides a framework for designing pervious surfaces, with detailed methods recommended where appropriate. A checklist of design considerations and information requirements is also provided. The importance of correct specification of materials is also discussed.

Appendix A1 provides case studies of the use of pervious surfaces for source control.

Appendix A2 discusses further research that is required.

Appendix A3 provides a design information checklist.

Appendix A4 provides information on maintenance requirements.

Appendix A5 discusses the factors that should be considered when deriving whole-life cost estimates for pervious pavements.

Appendix A6 gives additional detailed information relating to the water quality issues.

Appendix A7 looks at the adoption and legislation issues surrounding pervious surfaces.

The recommended design methodology is set out in Figure 6.1. To assist the reader in finding the relevant text when following this flow chart, key sections of text have been highlighted throughout the book.

1 Introduction

1.1 WHAT IS SOURCE CONTROL?

Source control can be defined as the control of runoff at or near its source. It is one of a series of disciplines and techniques that can be employed to develop a sustainable drainage system effectively. A proven concept in the development of a sustainable drainage system is the surface water management train (Figure 1.1). This reinforces, and wherever possible follows, the natural pattern of drainage. Ideally, drainage design should prevent problems occurring rather than providing mitigation measures to control water quality and the volume and rate of discharge.

The surface water management train utilises source control to minimise the problems associated with the traditional approach to drainage design, by controlling runoff where it is generated and returning it to the natural environment as soon as is reasonable. At each stage in the management train the flow and quality characteristics of the runoff are improved until it can be discharged.

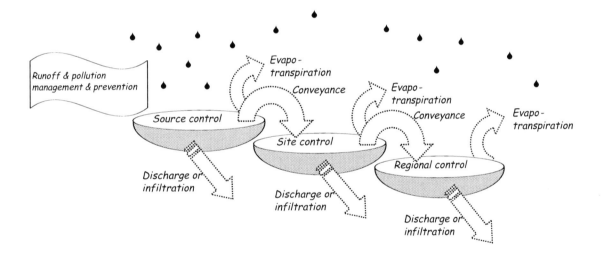

Figure 1.1 *Relationship between source control and overall surface water management train (CIRIA 2001a)*

Source control is to be preferred to controls elsewhere in the management train as it follows the natural drainage pattern, assigns the management of surface water to those causing the runoff and prevents problems arising rather than trying to mitigate them.

1.2 THE USE OF CONSTRUCTED PERVIOUS SURFACES AS A SOURCE CONTROL TECHNIQUE

As one of the primary methods of achieving source control, the use of pervious surfaces directly manages the quantity and quality of runoff at the earliest possible stage. Fundamental to the concept is the role played by the underlying layers for storage, infiltration (where possible), recycling and conveyance of surface water (Figure 1.2). These generally store and convey the surface water transmitted through the pervious surfacing (not the runoff). By definition, the runoff is that portion of the surface water that is NOT transmitted through the surfacing or subject to any other losses such as evaporation.

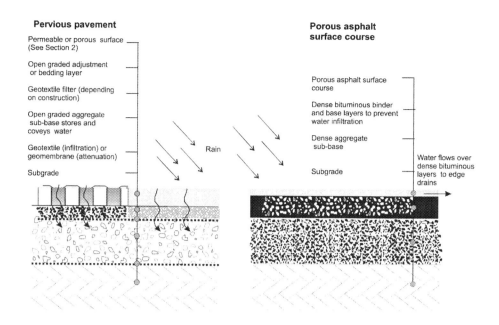

Figure 1.2 *Pervious pavement and porous asphalt surface course*

Constructed pervious surfaces remove or reduce the requirement for conventional drainage networks and ancillaries such as pipes, gully pots, manholes and interceptors.

The concept can be utilised for both infiltration and attenuation of surface water collected from paved (hard and soft landscaping) areas and roof catchments. As such it is suitable for incorporation into rainwater utilisation projects. Nevertheless, there are some limitations to the use of pervious surfaces (Box 1.1).

Box 1.1 *Locations for use of constructed pervious surfaces*

> The use of constructed pervious surfaces as a source control technique is currently limited to highways with low traffic volumes, low axle loads and speeds less than 30 mph limit, car parking areas and other lightly trafficked or non-trafficked surfaces. Many developments have a substantial area for car parking, which can be constructed with a pervious surface to attenuate runoff into local sewers or watercourses.
>
> In other countries, pervious surfaces have been used in some locations subject to heavy axle loads. The issues discussed in this publication will still be relevant, but at present such pavements should be designed on an individual basis in conjunction with experienced geotechnical and pavement engineers.
>
> The Highways Agency will not use pervious pavement systems for roads under their control. The potential failure of pervious pavements on high-speed roads, the safety implications of ponding and disruption arising from reconstruction are matters of particular concern.
>
> Infiltration techniques cannot be used below pervious surfaces in stormwater hotspots (Box 5.4).

1.3   BENEFITS OF CONSTRUCTED PERVIOUS SURFACES

The Environment Agency and Scottish Environment Protection Agency have policies to promote the use of SUDS, which are considered very important in reducing the effects of urban runoff on the environment (Box 1.2). This is reinforced by government planning guidance (PPG 25) that requires new developments to incorporate SUDS wherever possible. Pervious surfaces are an important source control technique that can be used either alone or together with other SUDS techniques.

The Scottish Environment Protection Agency and the Environment Agency for England and Wales are working together to reduce pollution and flooding risk, and to promote more sustainable drainage systems in Britain. There is no need for the drainage from urban developments to damage our water resources. However, to protect our environments, the Agencies need the support and co-operation of a wide range of public and private organisations involved in urban development – including planning and highway authorities, sewerage undertakers, and developers. By working together, it will be possible to ensure that drainage from roads and urban areas is designed in a cost-effective and more sustainable manner.

SUDS can be designed to fit into almost all urban settings, from hard surfaced areas to soft landscaped features, as a range of design options is available. Porous [pervious] pavement is an alternative to conventional paving in which water permeates through the paved structure rather than draining off it. Storage and filtering of the runoff water [occurs] and environmental benefits accrue.

Widespread adoption of these [SUDS] techniques in new developments would see a long-term improvement in the quality of our urban rivers, contributing to a more varied and attractive urban environment built on a sustainable basis.

NB: the publication refers to porous, rather than pervious, surfaces.

Planning Policy Guidance Note PPG3 requires housing developments to have a high density of dwellings. Industrial developments also usually require a high percentage of hard cover, and these issues are often perceived as a barrier to using SUDS techniques in urban situations. The use of pervious surfaces for car parks and similar areas is a valuable technique that should allow SUDS to be used more widely in urban situations, allowing the requirements of both PPG3 and PPG25 to be achieved.

The advantages of using pervious surfaces include:

* lower peak flows to watercourses, thereby reducing the risk of flooding downstream (Chapter 3)

* carefully designed, constructed and maintained surfaces lessen the effects of pollution in runoff on the environment (Chapter 5)

* they can be used in confined urban situations with a range of surface finishes that admit surface waters over their area of use

* a reduced need for deep excavations for drainage, which can have significant cost benefits, especially where disposal of contaminated soils is necessary

* as a drainage solution it is largely unrelated to the scale of the pervious surface, where the surface is often more than adequate to deal with the water falling on its own area

* flexibility – it is a solution that can be tailored so that construction costs suit the proposed usage and design life

* costs that are comparable to or lower than conventional surfacing and drainage solutions (providing all the costs are taken into account including items such as excavation and disposal of soils, discharge fees, cost of kerbs and gullies and removal of the need for large attenuation structures).

Pervious surfaces that are used in suitable locations and designed, constructed and adequately maintained following the guidance set out in this book should provide a cost-effective and durable source control technique.

Pervious surfaces may also appear as "soft" landscaping, as it is possible to "green" a surface using grass protection type systems. This ability has been recognised in Denmark, where there is a requirement on commercial/industrial areas for 15 per cent to be landscaping. This allows the inclusion of areas covered by grass protection systems, for example car parks.

In line with other hard surfacing products there is a range of surface colours and finishes for pervious surfaces, which offers choice to architects in site planning. The surface finish of pervious surfacing may vary from distinctly profiled (grass concrete) to smooth (porous macadam, porous or permeable paving blocks), making them suitable for a wide range of uses (Chapter 2).

In the broader planning of the urban landscape, the use of pervious structures for water storage for reuse may assist in the maintenance of plants, trees and shrubs. The use of stored rainwater, which is often less acidic, warmer and cheaper than treated mains water, is a further benefit available through the appropriate use of pervious structures.

Maintenance requirements for pervious pavements are no more onerous than those for conventional drainage, but they are different (Section 3.3 and Appendix A4). This should not prevent pervious surfacing being selected, as its other advantages in flood control, water reuse and groundwater recharge may have higher benefits, both on the curtilage and locality, as well as more widely in the environment. Pressure from regulators and planners may also mean that overall environmental considerations outweigh any perceived disadvantages and pervious pavements may be required to allow development to proceed.

1.4 DEFINITIONS

The terminology used regarding road pavements can be confusing due to differences between the United Kingdom, Europe and the USA. This is compounded by the use of some terms by the general public, for example tarmac as a general term for any tar- or bitumen-bound material.

The terms used in this publication are listed in Table 1.1 and accord with the forthcoming European standards being issued by the Comité Europeén de Normalisation (CEN).

Pervious surfaces within the context of source control provide the uppermost layer of pavement systems that are pervious throughout their entire construction depth. They allow water to infiltrate through the surfacing into the underlying sub-base and capping layers and, if required, into the foundation soils. Pervious surfaces for source control do not include conventional porous asphalt surfacing, which has been used in trials on some motorways and trunk roads to reduce spray and noise. This comprises a thin layer of porous asphalt over conventional impermeable materials (Figure 1.2).

Table 1.1   *Road pavement definitions adopted by CEN*

Road pavement	The load-bearing structure of a road (note the path at the side of a road, commonly referred to as a pavement, is the footway).
Carriageway	That part of the road used to carry vehicular traffic
Footway	Areas for pedestrians at the side of the carriageway
Bitumen	Hydrocarbon binder
Asphalt	All mixtures of mineral aggregates bound with bituminous materials used in the construction and maintenance of paved surfaces
Asphalt concrete	Macadams and Marshall Asphalt
Porous asphalt	An asphalt material used to make pavement layers pervious, with open voids to allow water to pass through (previously known as pervious macadam).
Surface course	Top layer of an asphalt pavement, known in UK as wearing course
Binder course	Second layer of an asphalt pavement, known in UK as basecourse
Base	Lowest bound layer of an asphalt pavement, known in UK as roadbase
Sub-base	Unbound layer of aggregate used immediately below bound layers
Capping layer	Unbound aggregate used to improve performance of foundation soils before laying sub-base

1.5   BACKGROUND TO PROJECT

Source control is a proven technique that can make a significant contribution to the improved management of surface water. The Environment Agency, SEPA, local authorities and the UK Government are actively promoting the widespread uptake of sustainable drainage techniques, as this will assist in the long-term reduction of flood risk, improve water quality, contribute to water resources locally and provide aesthetic and amenity benefits. Additionally, source control can assist with the recovery of depleted ground water levels (via infiltration) and the stabilisation of fluctuating river levels.

CIRIA's recent projects on best practice and design guidance on the implementation of sustainable drainage systems have identified various barriers to the use of source control, including a lack of specific guidance on scientific approaches to the design and construction of pervious surfaces. There has been minimal independent guidance on the subject and this lack of information has led, in some cases, to inappropriate design and misinterpretation of the structural and hydraulic performance requirements of constructed pervious surfaces.

In addition to the shortage of information, the traditional approach to pavement design has been to minimise the ingress of water into the underlying layers rather than to allow infiltration and storage under the surface.

1.6 PURPOSE AND SCOPE OF THIS BOOK

This publication provides authoritative guidance on the appropriate approach to the successful design and construction of pervious surfaces.

The book will also provide an improved understanding of the hydraulic, structural and water quality performance issues of constructed pervious surfaces based on information available. The current level of knowledge about some of the design and performance issues varies, and in some cases rigorous analysis is not possible. This is true in other areas of engineering and should not be a barrier to the use of pervious pavements. Where necessary, conservative assumptions and judgement based on observed performance can be used to allow the design to proceed.

The book provides sufficient design guidance to enable both specifiers and constructors of pervious pavements to adopt a more scientifically based approach to their use as an effective stormwater source control technique. Pervious pavements designed in accordance with the note should:

- deal with stormwater in an acceptable manner by helping to maintain runoff rates from developments at pre-development levels
- carry the required traffic loads without structural failure occurring
- minimise the risk of causing pollution to controlled waters.

This should facilitate the wider use of pervious surfaces as a source control technique and avoid failures due to inappropriate construction. The book explains how designers can ensure that the pervious surface and the construction below can effectively and safely store and transmit water while reliably supporting the design traffic loads.

It is not intended that this book should be a detailed guide to either hydraulic design of drainage systems or the structural design of pavements. It discusses only those aspects of hydraulic and structural design that are directly affected by the use of pervious surfaces as source control. Where necessary, reference is made to other publications that describe design methods suitable for application to pervious surfaces.

Sustainable urban drainage systems include other techniques, such as swales, infiltration trenches and lagoons, which are not covered by this book. Nor does it cover the design of porous asphalt surfacing layers used on high-speed roads (see Figure 1.2).

As a result of this work, further research needs have been identified. These are detailed in Appendix A2.

1.7 SOURCES OF INFORMATION

This publication has been compiled from information gained from undertaking a worldwide literature review covering all aspects of constructed pervious surfaces. In addition, consultation has been sought with a diverse range of consultants, contractors and manufacturers/distributors to gain the widest possible view.

The research has been reviewed and agreed by a dedicated steering group comprising experienced individuals from many disciplines.

1.8 ASSOCIATED PUBLICATIONS

This book provides independent guidance on the development of a more scientific approach to the design, construction and maintenance of constructed pervious surfaces.

The following publications are relevant in terms of additional information:

- *Barriers, liners and cover systems for containment and control of land contamination*, CIRIA Special Publication 124 (Privett *et al*, 1996). Provides information relating to the specification and construction of geomembrane liners.

- *Control of pollution from highway drainage discharges*, CIRIA Report 142 (Luker and Montague, 1994). Provides information on the water quality of highway runoff.

- *Infiltration drainage, manual of good practice*, CIRIA Report 156 (Bettess, 1996). Provides method of rainfall estimation and design method for infiltration below pervious pavements.

- *Sustainable urban drainage systems, design manual for Scotland and Northern Ireland*, CIRIA C521 (CIRIA, 2000a). Background information on design of pervious surfaces, as one element of a sustainable urban drainage system.

- *Sustainable urban drainage systems, design manual for England and Wales*, CIRIA C522 (CIRIA, 2000b). Background information on design of pervious surfaces, as one element of a sustainable urban drainage system.

- *Sustainable urban drainage systems, best practice manual*, CIRIA C523 (CIRIA, 2001a). Background information on pervious surfaces, as one element of a sustainable urban drainage system.

- *Planning Policy Guidance Note PPG25, Development and flood risk*. Department for Transport, Local Government and the Regions.

2 Constructed pervious surface drainage systems

2.1 MAIN TYPES OF CONSTRUCTED PERVIOUS SURFACES

Pervious surfaces can be either porous or permeable. The important distinction between the two is:

- **porous surfacing** infiltrates water across the entire surface of the material forming the surface, for example grass and gravel surfaces, porous concrete and porous asphalt
- **permeable surfacing** is formed of material that is itself impervious to water but, by virtue of voids formed through the surface, allows infiltration through the pattern of voids, for example concrete block paving.

There are many different variations of each type that are commercially available.

2.1.1 Porous surfacing options

Examples of porous surfacing and typical locations where each type of construction is used are provided below.

Open-textured soil or granular material

Gravel or similar surface on a sub-base. Typically used in locations where very low volumes of lightweight traffic, such as cars, will be present and a low-cost solution is required. There is little design and the use is restricted to locations such as pedestrian areas, driveways on private property and temporary car parks (Figure 2.1). Geosynthetic cellular confinement systems (a three-dimensional honeycomb of flexible perforated plastic strips infilled with gravel) are sometimes used as reinforcement for the sub-base below a gravel surface (Section 4.7.1). The honeycomb confines the gravel to allow heavier loading to be carried on unsurfaced roads or car parks.

Figure 2.1   *Granular surfaced car park*

Geosynthetic gravel/grass protection systems

Modular interlocking plastic paving systems infilled with gravel/grass/aggregate and bedded on a free-draining structural sub-base layer. Typically used for light/medium loadings such as car parks or locations where occasional heavy vehicular loadings occur (for example, from refuse collection vehicles, removal lorries or fire appliances). Typical details are shown in Figure 2.2

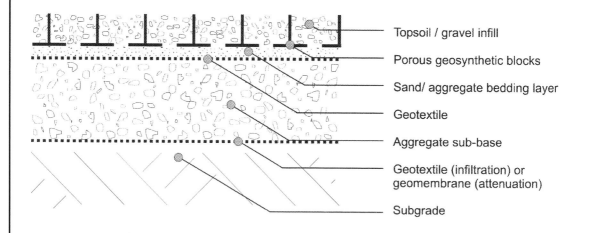

- Topsoil / gravel infill
- Porous geosynthetic blocks
- Sand/ aggregate bedding layer
- Geotextile
- Aggregate sub-base
- Geotextile (infiltration) or geomembrane (attenuation)
- Subgrade

Figure 2.2   *Geosynthetic gravel/grass protection system*

Small porous elemental surfacing blocks

Precast blocks formed of low-fines concrete or other material, which results in the blocks having many small, interlinked internal voids throughout their section. These are laid on a recommended sub-base, which has in the past varied from Type 1 sub-base (relatively impermeable) to clean gravel and crushed rock, or other open-textured support. These remain free-draining provided regular maintenance keeps the surface void spaces and joints between blocks free of debris. Typical uses are for public, engineered surfaces carrying light loading but of high frequency such as shopping centre car parks. Typical details are provided in Figure 2.3.

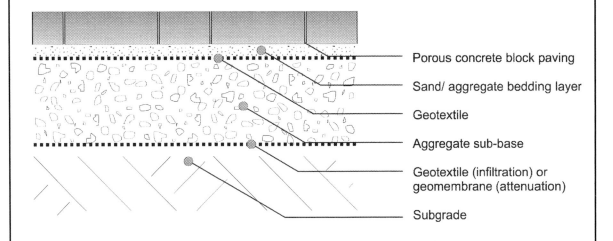

Porous concrete block paving

Sand/ aggregate bedding layer

Geotextile

Aggregate sub-base

Geotextile (infiltration) or geomembrane (attenuation)

Subgrade

Figure 2.3   *Small porous elemental surfacing blocks*

Continuous-laid porous material

Porous asphalt, porous concrete or resin-bound aggregate, laid on a recommended sub-base of free-draining granular material. Remains free-draining provided regular surface maintenance limits the deposit of debris in the surface void spaces. Typical uses are for public, engineered surfaces carrying high volumes of heavy and/or light loading, such as shopping centre car parks and service roads. (Note that this differs from the use of porous asphalt as a thin surfacing layer to reduce spray on conventional high-speed roads). Typical details are shown in Figure 2.4.

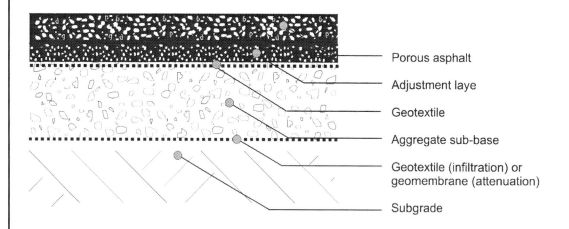

- Porous asphalt
- Adjustment laye
- Geotextile
- Aggregate sub-base
- Geotextile (infiltration) or geomembrane (attenuation)
- Subgrade

Figure 2.4   *Continuous-laid porous material*

2.1.2 Permeable surfacing options

Examples are:

Large elemental surfacing blocks

Precast concrete blocks with a pattern of voids intended for filling with soil, which allow for the growth of grass (grass concrete), laid on a recommended sub-base. These may remain relatively free-draining provided trafficking does not compact the earth fill within the void spaces. Typical uses are for low-cost, temporary or occasional usage roadways and parking areas where vehicular loading is generally light and where the appearance of a grassed surface is seen as environmentally desirable, such as car parks and fire access routes. Details are provided in Figure 2.5.

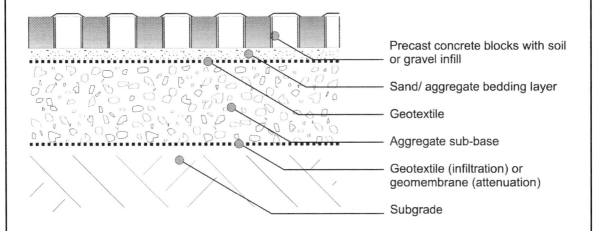

Precast concrete blocks with soil or gravel infill

Sand/ aggregate bedding layer

Geotextile

Aggregate sub-base

Geotextile (infiltration) or geomembrane (attenuation)

Subgrade

Figure 2.5   *Large elemental surfacing blocks*

Small elemental surfacing blocks

Precast concrete blocks with a pattern of indentations along their edges intended to be filled with sharp sand/gravel, laid on a recommended sub-base, which should be of single-size crushed rock or other open-textured support. This remains free-draining provided surface maintenance limits the deposit of debris in the indentations and joints between blocks. Typical uses are for public engineered surfaces carrying high volumes of light vehicular loading, such as shopping centre car parks (Figure 2.6).

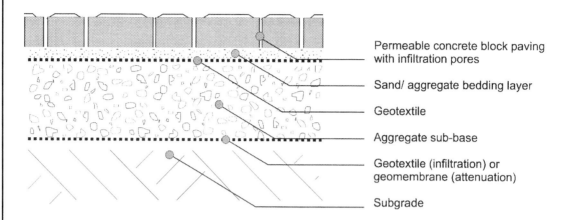

Permeable concrete block paving with infiltration pores

Sand/ aggregate bedding layer

Geotextile

Aggregate sub-base

Geotextile (infiltration) or geomembrane (attenuation)

Subgrade

Figure 2.6 *Small elemental surfacing blocks*

Continuous-laid permeable material

In-situ cast concrete systems are available that provide a surface with large voids for infiltration, while offering hardstanding for vehicles. The surface is unsuitable for small-wheeled trolleys and pedestrian use over large areas and has limitations aesthetically. Typically used in car parking areas (Figure 2.7).

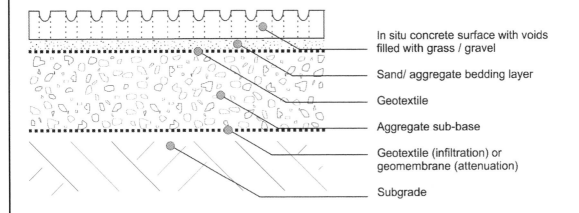

In situ concrete surface with voids filled with grass / gravel

Sand/ aggregate bedding layer

Geotextile

Aggregate sub-base

Geotextile (infiltration) or geomembrane (attenuation)

Subgrade

Figure 2.7   *Continuous-laid permeable material*

2.2   CONSTRUCTION OPTIONS

Contributing catchment. Often pervious areas are required only to handle rainfall landing directly upon their surfaces, but their capacity may be sufficient to allow their use as a drainage path for water discharged from adjacent areas, such as roofs or impermeable areas of car park (Figure 2.8). It is advisable to release any additional waters either on to the surface of the pervious construction, or via a debris trap, so as to prevent clogging of the sub-surface layers.

Figure 2.8   *Roof downpipe discharging to porous asphalt pavement*

This process must be limited to the capacity of the pervious structure unless it is increased to meet adjacent surface inflows. An example of this approach is the use of the porous car park sub-base at Bognor Regis Sports Centre (case study in Appendix A1), where adjacent sports buildings and roadways, totalling some 700 m² impermeable area, are drained into 300 m² plan area of car park. The runoff is all infiltrated to ground, avoiding localised overloading of the sewer system (Carpenter, 2000).

Surface gradient. Traditionally, impervious surfaces have been laid with slopes to direct surface waters to inlets. Pervious surfaces perform best when horizontal with local rainfall intercepted at source. This avoids establishing crossfalls or false crowns and ensures simpler, more economic site construction. There may be limits to the slope of the surface generally to ensure surface water interception. On sloping sites, pervious surfaces may be terraced to accommodate differences in levels.

Surface water storage. Where the pervious surface is designed to allow for surface storage (Box 3.2) small bunds may be used to contain surface flow. Standard 250 mm by 125 mm kerbs do this satisfactorily with only a small ramp required at the roadway entrance. The gradient of the pervious surface should, where possible, remain level to minimise flow concentrations to specific areas of the surface to reduce of ponding. The acceptability of this depends on the final land usage. For example, it may be acceptable on a low-usage boat park area, but be unacceptable in a busy city-centre car park.

Internal water storage. Pervious constructions have been used for the internal storage of water for reuse or slow release to outfall. To achieve this, the sides and base of the underlying layers should be lined with an impermeable geomembrane and any penetrations through geomembrane should be sealed with proprietary collars formed from the same material as the geomembrane liner to prevent leakage. Also, where subgrade conditions are unsuitable for infiltration and repeated wetting, an underlying geomembrane with an outflow facility may be necessary.

The stored waters may be removed for various reuse applications such as irrigation, toilet flushing etc, although an overflow will be required to release excess water safely. This approach reduces the waters recharging the groundwater and reduces demand on potable water supplies, which may be a significant saving in some parts of the UK. Further guidance is provided in CIRIA publication C539 (CIRIA, 2001b) and CIRIA Project Report 80 (CIRIA, 2001c).

Because the storage volume needed for attenuation must empty in a reasonable period to allow inflow from later storms, the same storage volume should not be used for both attenuation and reuse. This is because there is no guarantee the storage for reuse will be empty when it is required to attenuate flows due to stormwater.

2.3 CONSTRUCTION BELOW PERVIOUS SURFACES

Dependent upon the surface material and use of the surface, the underlying construction may be:

- soil, sharp sand, crushed rock
- one or more layers of different materials, eg granular and/or geosynthetic layers
- include a permeable geotextile or an impervious geomembrane.

It may also include, if necessary, drainage networks to discharge water entering or flowing through the construction.

The outflow from the pervious pavement construction can be achieved by:

- directing water within the construction to a drainage network either on the subgrade or within the permeable sub-base, which conveys it to a suitable outfall or disposal point (Figure 2.9a)
- allowing water entering the pervious surface to infiltrate down into the groundwater through the base of the construction (Figure 2.9b)
- letting water discharge at the base of the construction and pass slowly to groundwater, and releasing excess waters that would otherwise fill the construction via a high-level overflow pipe (Figure 2.9b)
- storing water in the construction for suitable non-potable use, any excess being disposed of via a high-level overflow pipe.

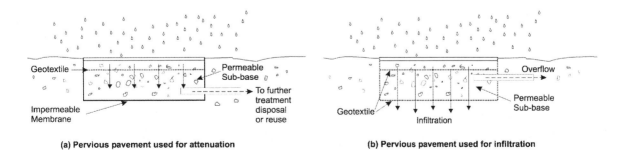

(a) Pervious pavement used for attenuation   (b) Pervious pavement used for infiltration

Figure 2.9   *Outflow options*

The construction adopted will be dependent on site-specific constraints such as limits on discharges to outfalls, the risk of causing groundwater pollution, the return period of the design rainfall event and the infiltration capacity of the natural soils.

The use of a sealed impermeable liner to the pavement structure facilitates the containment and treatment of isolated spillages. The outflow water quality issues are very important and are covered in more detail in Chapter 5.

2.4 USE OF CONSTRUCTED PERVIOUS SURFACES IN THE UNITED KINGDOM

A brief summary of the development of constructed pervious surfaces is given in Box 2.1.

Box 2.1   *Development of pervious surfaces in the United Kingdom*

1 American experience in the 1970s and 1980s with porous concrete and macadam.
2 Swedish use of porous macadam in 1980s and 1990s.
3 Japanese developments since 1980s, including experiments with high-temperature treatment of sewage sludge to form paving slabs of resulting "glass bead" type material.
4 French experience with porous concrete and macadam in Bordeaux and development of reservoir structures with porous macadam surfacing in the Nantes and Paris areas.
5 Long-term UK usage of grass concrete systems for temporary or low-cost surfacing, which developed in 1980s into research into small-element concrete blocks forming permeable surfaces at Nottingham Trent and Coventry Universities, with first public usage at Shire Hall, Reading in 1988.
6 Initiative by SEPA for techniques to provide treatment of stormwater led to search for suitable systems, of which pervious pavements was seen as one, based upon continuing research.
7 Mid-1990s saw first public commercial site in UK using porous asphalt as part of a pervious system for source control at Tesco, Wokingham.
8 First UK commercial porous block paving launched in 1998, subsequently withdrawn and replaced by permeable block designs and leading to some 400 000 m² sales by 2001.

Below is a list of selected UK and overseas case studies of projects in which some form of pervious surfacing has been used. All have benefited from varying levels of post-installation monitoring providing feedback on their in-life performance.

- Bognor Regis, Sports Centre
- National Air Traffic Services, Edinburgh
- Royal Bank of Scotland, Edinburgh
- Tesco, Wokingham
- Wheatley MSA, M40, Oxford
- Powells Creek, Concord, New South Wales, Australia.

The case studies appear in Appendix A1, which provides more detailed information. Although pervious surfaces are installed in many sites, in relatively few has *in-situ* monitoring of the hydraulic, water quality or structural performance been undertaken. This is particularly true where infiltration is used, due to the difficulty of measuring the flow and quality of water in the ground below the pavement.

2.5 CURRENT DESIGN APPROACHES

Historical and current design approaches for trafficked pervious surfaces have generally been developed by the use of methods based on a combination of manufacturers' recommendations and designers' views on the relevance or otherwise of traditional design methods for non-pervious pavements.

This uncertain approach has sometimes resulted in confusion and loss of confidence in the design and construction of this type of surfacing. The present publication should help prevent the under- and over-design that has occurred in the past and improve confidence in the technical and commercial viability of the concept.

3 Hydraulic performance issues

3.1 URBAN HYDROLOGY

3.1.1 Rainfall runoff processes

When rain first lands on an impermeable surface it first wets it, with some of the rain being absorbed, after which some of the rain may form puddles in depressions on the surface. This process will continue for a short period after which time the rain begins to flow over the surface towards drainage inlets. The time taken for rainwater to reach an inlet from all parts of a traditional impermeable surfaces will vary from two or three up to 10–15 minutes (National Water Council and Department of the Environment, 1981) dependent upon the intensity of the rainfall and the gradient of the surface. This time is called the time of entry.

The amount of rain required to land on a surface before runoff begins is called the initial rainfall loss, or depression storage, and is typically under 1 mm for impermeable surfaces.

Runoff from building roofs, which generally have steep slopes, runs off into the drainage system very quickly. Typically very high rates of flow occur over a short duration, particularly if siphonic roof drainage systems are used.

Most types of impermeable urban surface do not discharge all the rainfall that lands on them after the time of entry has been exceeded, as they have joints and cracks that allow leakage through the surface during runoff. It is generally assumed that this leakage is a constant proportion of the rainfall, once runoff starts, known as the runoff coefficient. The volumetric runoff coefficient can be defined as a measure of the amount of rainfall that is converted to runoff. In natural situations with no impervious cover, the runoff coefficient is typically in the 0.05–0.10 range. A surface fully paved with conventional surfacing materials can increase this to 0.90 (CIRIA, 2001b).

If the amounts of rain and runoff for several storms are plotted on a graph, the average values of initial loss and of the runoff coefficient for a particular surface can be determined (Figure 3.1). The runoff coefficient for the asphalt concrete in this case is 0.984 (98.4 per cent) and the initial rainfall loss is 0.424 mm (Jacobson and Harremoes, 1981).

In a pervious pavement system, the rain falling on it infiltrates across the entire surface and is then conveyed through the underlying layers. This has the effect of reducing the runoff (or outflow) from the system and increases the initial losses (Box 3.5). For a porous block pavement the runoff coefficient from the system in Figure 3.1 is 0.677 (67.7 per cent) and the initial rainfall loss is 1.650 mm (Schluter and Jefferies, 2001).

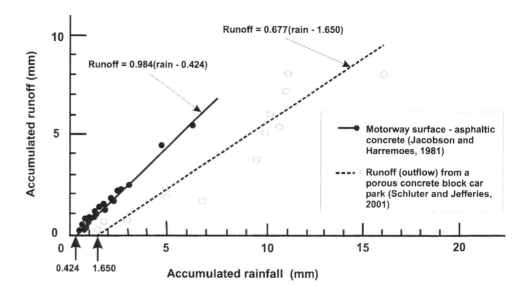

Figure 3.1 *Runoff coefficients*

If the amount of runoff in a particular storm is compared with the amount of rainfall for that storm, it is possible to determine a measurement known as the percentage runoff. It is likely that a wide range of answers for the percentage runoff will be obtained if this calculation is undertaken for several storms for the same surface. This is because the response of the surface will vary according to whether the surface was still wet from a previous rainfall and the duration of the rainfall, for example. The initial loss from the rainfall on a surface also varies with these factors, but it is generally assumed that the runoff coefficient remains unchanged for a particular surface.

The efficient removal of runoff from impermeable urban surfaces is assisted by laying surfaces with crossfalls and channels to direct flows to drainage inlets. When a surface is nearly horizontal, the correct profiling of the surface becomes important if runoff is to be directed to inlets. The runoff hydrograph into the drainage inlet varies with the nature of the rainfall. However an impermeable surface hydrograph usually shows:

- that runoff begins soon after rainfall begins
- that the time taken for the surface to drain after rain stops is short
- that the total volume of runoff is often some 80–95 per cent of the rainfall volume (Figure 3.2).

In the hydrograph shown in Figure 3.2 runoff starts after 0.5 mm of rainfall and is completed some 10 minutes after the end of rainfall (Pratt *et al*, 1984).

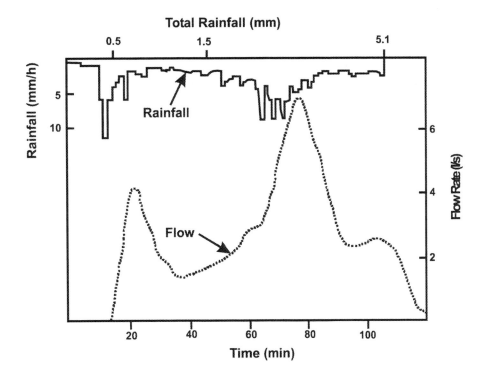

Figure 3.2   *Typical runoff hydrograph for an impermeable surface (Pratt* et al, *1984)*

Overall, impermeable surfaces respond quickly once rain starts to fall and discharge almost all the rainwater during, or soon after, the period of rainfall. The consequence of this performance is that properly laid, puddle-free impermeable surfaces shed runoff rapidly into the receiving drainage systems.

Runoff from impermeable urban surfaces also washes off from the surface any pollution thatderives from sources such as atmospheric deposits, oil leaks from cars and tyre wear. The majority is washed off at the beginning of a rainfall event (CIRIA, 2000a) and this is known as the first flush. In this regard, sloping roof surfaces make the most significant contribution to the first discharges within the drainage system, but subsequent contributions from the paved surfaces deliver the more significant pollution contribution (Figure 3.3).

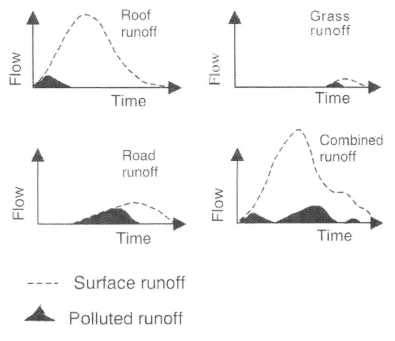

Figure 3.3   *Contribution of flow and pollution from urban surfaces (CIRIA, 2000a)*

3.1.2 Modification of rainfall runoff process with pervious surfaces

Pervious surfaces allow rainwater to infiltrate across their entire surface. This process removes the need to construct crossfalls to direct waters to drainage inlets. Whereas impermeable surfaces drain most efficiently when laid to a gradient, pervious surfaces are most advantageous when laid horizontally, so that rainfall infiltrates where it hits the surface with no tendency to flow laterally. However, even when laid at gradients up to 10 per cent, laboratory results have shown rapid infiltration can occur with limited downslope movement on a pervious surface, even in the presence of silts (Scott, 2001).

Once the rainwater has entered the pervious surface it may flow out of the construction through the base to groundwater or, if the construction is undersealed, the waters will be intercepted by a drainage network and discharged from the sub-base to a suitable receiving drainage system. Comparison of the outflow hydrograph at the drain outlet from an impermeable surface (Figure 3.2) with that for a drain receiving outflows from an impermeable surface (Figure 3.4) reveals marked differences in performance.

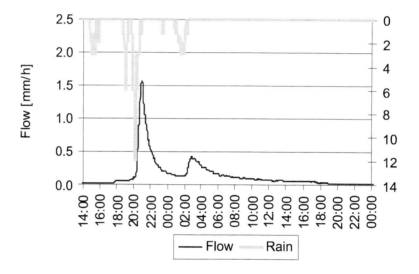

Figure 3.4 *Graph of flow against time for porous pavement at Royal Bank of Scotland (Schluter and Jefferies, 2001)*

The porous surface and its sub-structure responds to rainfall more slowly than does the impermeable surface and continues to discharge for much longer, hours and even days after rainfall stops. On Figure 3.4 the first outflow from the porous surface was some three hours after start of rainfall and discharge continued into a second day, although there were additional, smaller rainfalls within the event. This effect is known as attenuation.

Further detailed discussion of the effects of attenuation and the influence of the type of construction is provided in Box 3.1.

The difference between runoff hydrographs for impermeable and pervious surfaces is also demonstrated in Figure CS2.2 provided in Case Study No 2 (Appendix A1).

Box 3.1   *Attenuation by pervious surfaces*

Because of the delay in discharging all waters from a rainfall event, a second rainfall may occur during the runoff and hydrographs become overlapped (see Figure 3.5)

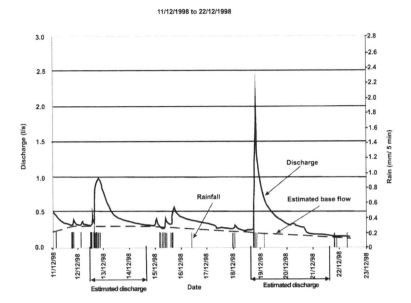

Figure 3.5   *Hydrograph for a pervious pavement over several rainfall events (Abbott et al, 2000)*

The hydrographs may then appear similar to those that occur in a natural stream catchment, in which there is a base flow onto which storm hydrographs are superimposed. There is further similarity with a natural stream catchment as the delay in first discharge from the pervious structure and the total volume of discharge are influenced by antecedent conditions, as are natural catchments (see Table 3.1).

Table 3.1   *Comparison of rainfall events on a permeable car park with similar rainfall depth, but differing antecedent conditions (Pratt et al, 1995)*

Event no	Rainfall, mm	Percentage runoff, %	Antecedent rainfall, mm	Duration of dry period, hours
7323	9.1	41	2	10
7349	9.0	25	1	250

Observations of outflow hydrographs for the Wheatley (M40) motorway service area showed that on average only 22.5 per cent of the runoff actually left the system during the storm and only some 67 per cent ever discharged; storm events lasting some 5.65 hours on average took 2.3 days on average to drain away; and the peak outflow was significantly reduced, for example, the peak discharge was equivalent to 0.37 mm/h (0.88 l/s/ha) for a peak rainfall intensity of 12 mm/h (33.3 l/s/ha) (Abbott *et al*, 2002)

When rainfall enters a pervious surface and the underlying sub-base, the outflow hydrograph will be influenced by the way the construction materials retain or delay flow. Comparing values for the initial loss and the runoff coefficient between impermeable and pervious surfaces shows further differences (Figure 3.1). For a permeable surface with four different sub-base materials beneath it in Nottingham, the initial loss, the runoff coefficient and the percentage runoff on average varied with the sub-base material, other features in the constructions being the same (see Table 3.2).

Table 3.2   *Rainfall runoff characteristics for a permeable car park at Nottingham with four different sub-base materials (Pratt et al, 1995)*

Sub-base material	Initial loss	Runoff coefficient	Percentage runoff, %
Gravel (10 mm rounded)	3.0	0.69	37
Blast furnace slag (40 mm)	3.2	0.68	34
Granite (5 mm to 40 mm)	2.4	0.76	47
Carboniferous limestone aggregate (5 mm to 40 mm)	2.8	0.81	45

For a porous-surfaced car park in Edinburgh the initial loss and runoff coefficient were 1.6 mm and 0.68 mm respectively. At another site in Edinburgh where the porous surface was not undersealed, allowing infiltration, the initial loss was some 5.3 mm (Boon, 2000).

A pervious surface and its sub-structure may therefore significantly modify outflow hydrographs to drainage systems. Downstream impacts are minimised too unless there is surface runoff in extreme storm conditions. The rainwater may either be infiltrated through the surface and into the sub-soil, or retained within the pervious construction. Retention can be achieved by installing an impermeable geomembrane to the base and sides of the underlying construction to form a tank structure.

3.2 HYDRAULIC DESIGN CRITERIA

3.2.1 Rainfall intensity/surface infiltration

The rate of infiltration through the surface must exceed the design maximum rainfall intensity, if surface ponding of rainwater is to be avoided. Surface ponding is not necessarily a problem, provided it is planned for in the surface design (Box 3.2) and the maximum water depth on the surface and the time for which it remains are acceptable in the situation. Clearly the use of surface storage is limited to pervious surfaces in locations used by pedestrians and slow speed or standing vehicles.

Box 3.2   *Planning for surface storage*

> The idea of planning for surface storage of rainwater is rarely incorporated into current designs, but in the context of horizontal pervious surfaces it should be considered. Rainfall of 10 mm may be seen as a significant event, but even if this were all to remain on the pervious surface it would present inconvenience but no danger. If only a millimetre or two remains on the surface of a car park for a brief period, the size of the problem is insignificant. The occurence should not be seen as a failure of the system, provided it has been designed for it from the outset and it may provide additional flood protection for downstream areas.
>
> In these circumstances the owner/occupier must be made fully aware of the implications of the design and likely duration and frequency of flooding, as this may be classed as failure if the owner/occupier found this unacceptable.

With reinforced grass protection systems, the soil within the voids may absorb and retain rainfall for subsequent evaporation/transpiration by the grass. This is an important mechanism in the reduction of runoff, which is not normally considered within current design practice. Typically, precast concrete blocks absorb 4–5 mm rain, which may subsequently evaporate (Bond *et al*, 1999). Conversely, for a highway the presence of a millimetre or two of water, even for a brief period will be unacceptable on safety grounds.

A simple method of assessing the levels of rainfall in the UK is provided in CIRIA Report 156, *Infiltration drainage – manual of good practice* (Bettess, 1996). The uncertainties of internal water movements in pervious pavements mean that, although more complex analyses may be available, this simple method is appropriate (Box 3.3).

Design rainfall events are described in terms of rainfall intensity, duration and frequency (return period) of the event, for example 25 mm/h for one hour with a frequency of five years. Statistical values of these parameters for a given location can be obtained from the *Flood Studies Report* by the Institute of Hydrology (1975) or from the Meteorological Office.

The Environment Agency manages flood risk over a catchment and will assess the risk arising from a development when specifying the standard of attenuation that is required at a site. In the areas of highest risk this may equate to a storm return period of 100 years or more being managed by the surface water drainage system within a site. Early discussions should be carried out with the relevant drainage authority so that the required return period is known before design work starts.

The hydrograph is simplified to a constant distribution of intensity over the given duration and all the rainfall is assumed to pass immediately into the pervious pavement system with no attenuation occurring. This is a conservative method and should provide a built-in safety factor to designs.

The *Flood Estimation Handbook* (FEH) (Institute of Hydrology, 1999) is a recent publication, providing guidance on rainfall and river flood frequency estimation in the UK. The FEH is generally concerned with large catchment areas for rivers. It does, however, provide information on extreme rainfall events in the UK. It also includes a new method for estimating the rainfall depth of a given rarity over a given duration for a point or catchment anywhere in the UK. Due to the uncertainties in some aspects of the performance of pervious surfaces the method is currently too complex to be recommended for the routine design of these systems.

Box 3.3   *Calculating design rainfall*

Following the method described in CIRIA Report 156 (Bettess, 1996)

For a given return period, the volume of rainfall falling on to the pervious pavement is given by:

Volume of runoff = $Q.D = i.A_d.D$

Where:

i = rainstorm intensity (m/h)
D = rainstorm duration (h)
A_d = area to be drained (m²)
Q = inflow (m³/h)

Drainage systems are usually designed to a specific return period. The selection of the return period is determined by the consequences of failure, and a return period appropriate to the risk should be selected. This should take account of the use of the pervious surface, the disruption that will be caused by flooding, owner requirements and safety issues, for example. The changing rainfall patterns resulting from climate change should also be considered.

As stated previously, drainage authorities in many areas may require surface water drainage designs to deal with return periods of 100 years, although historically a return period of 10 years has been adopted for the design of soakaways.

At a particular location, for a specified return period, the rainfall depth varies with duration of storm event. This relationship between depth and duration varies across the country and so attention must be paid to the geographic location of the system.

The Institute of Hydrology has carried out an extensive analysis of rainfall statistics and has provided a method to determine the relationship between depth, duration and return period (Institute of Hydrology, 1975), which forms the basis of the method described in CIRIA Report 156.

The notation MT-D is used to identify a storm, where:
M is the depth of rain in millimetres
T is the return period in years
D is the storm duration.

Thus M10-15 minutes is the depth of rainfall of a 10-year return period storm event of 15 minutes' duration.

Continued on next page...

Box 3.3

Box 3.3   *Calculating design rainfall (continued)*

The appropriate storm duration used in calculations should relate to the system or facility of concern. If the purpose of the storm selected is to analyse a local drainage system, then something close to the time of concentration of the system, such as a 15-minute duration, would be used to define the storm. If the storm is used to analyse a large city-wide system within a 12-hour time of concentration plus the routeing through large-diameter storage facilities, then a 24-hour-duration storm may be more appropriate.

Determine the values of design rainfall depth (M), intensity (i), and duration (D) using Figure 3.6 and Table 3.3 for storms of different duration with a 10-year return period.

Step 1
Determine the rainfall ratio, r, for the location of the system, interpolating between contours. Note r is the ratio of the 60 minutes to two-day rainfall of a five-year return period.

Step 2
Using the value of r from Step 1 determine the 10-year rainfall intensity, M10, for the required duration of storm, from Table 3.3, interpolating as required. Where other dimensions are in m the rainfall intensity should be expressed in m/h for consistency.

Repeat steps 1 and 2 for variety of durations to obtain a set of values of i and D for a 10-year return period. If rainfall intensities for a different return period are required the growth curves in the *Flood Studies Report* (Institute of Hydrology, 1975) should be used. These relate the value for a 10-year return period for those for different return periods.

Step 3
Using the storm duration and intensity determine the critical combination that produces the maximum volume of water to be stored, given the outflow from the system during the storm.

Example
Determine the 10-year return period rainfall statistics for a site near Southampton, with no outflow during the storm.

Step 1 – From this map Figure 3.6 the value of r is 0.35
Step 2 – Using r = 0.35 and Table 3.3

Storm duration, D (min) required	Rainfall intensity, i (m/h)	Volume of storage (m^3/m^2 area
10	0.074	0.012
15	0.061	0.015
30	0.039	0.020
60	0.025	0.025
120	0.015	0.030
360	0.009	0.054
600	0.005	0.050

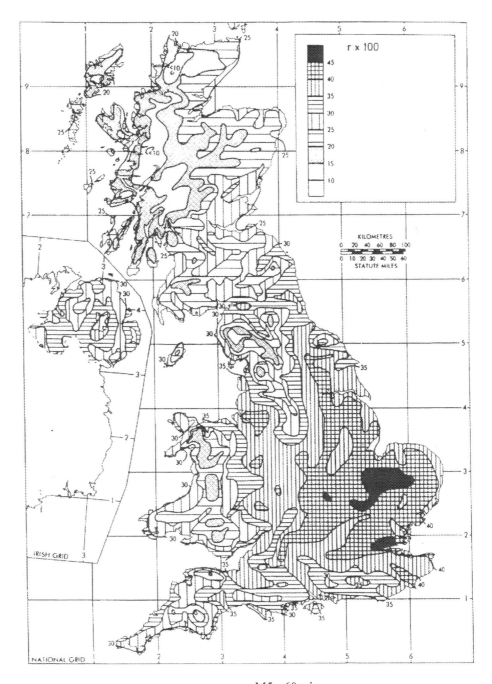

Figure 3.6 *Values of rainfall ratio r in UK* ($r = \dfrac{M5 - 60\,\mathrm{min}}{M5 - 2\,day}$) *(Bettess, 1996)*

Table 3.3   *M10 rainfall intensity (mm/h) for duration, D, and ratio, r (England and Wales) (Bettess, 1996)*

	Rainfall duration (D)									
	Minutes				Hours					
r	5	10	15	30	1	2	4	6	10	24
0.12	62.9	49	43.16	33	24.8	18.1	12.8	10.6	8.44	5.65
0.15	71.4	55.2	46.8	39.2	24.8	17.5	12	9.59	7.43	4.61
0.18	77.2	59.5	49.8	35.2	24.8	16.7	11.2	8.85	6.63	4.08
0.21	82.8	62.5	52.7	36.2	24.8	16.4	10.6	8.41	6.13	3.42
0.24	89.3	67.3	54.6	37.2	24.8	16.1	10.3	7.93	5.62	3.21
0.27	95	70.3	57.1	37.7	24.8	15.7	9.92	7.52	5.29	2.97
0.3	97.9	71.8	58	38.2	24.8	15.5	9.58	7.12	5.05	2.75
0.33	100	73.2	60	38.7	24.8	15.2	9.33	6.98	4.85	2.53
0.36	104	74.6	61	39.2	24.8	15.1	9.03	6.73	4.56	2.36
0.39	107	76.1	62	39.7	24.8	15	8.9	6.53	4.37	2.24
0.42	111	77.6	63	40.2	24.8	14.9	8.73	6.38	4.21	2.12
0.45	114	79.1	64	40.7	24.8	14.8	8.49	6.14	4.07	2.01

Drainage systems are usually designed based on return periods. For example, a return period of 10 years means that, on average, the maximum design rainfall event will be exceeded once every 10 years and flooding will occur (the level of flooding can be determined for the given return period). This can also be expressed as an annual probability of exceedance, which for a 10-year return period is 1/10 or 10 per cent (a 10 per cent chance that flooding will occur in any given year).

It is usually not economical to provide a pervious pavement (or any other conventional drainage system) that can cope with all rainfall events, and periodic failure is accepted. The return period should be selected on the basis of the acceptability and consequences of failure. If human life is likely to be endangered by any flooding the design should be based on storms of greater intensity than have been recorded in that location, to give a factor of safety. The level of flooding and likely frequency should be made clear and agreed with all affected parties, such as the occupier and adopting authorities. The safety of surrounding developments should also be considered as part of this process.

Surface materials such as porous concrete and porous asphalt generally have rates of infiltration that greatly exceed the design rainfall intensity (Box 3.4). The surface infiltration rate can be affected by factors such as clogging and the presence of less permeable layers within the construction, although the evidence does suggest that they can continue to perform adequately without maintenance in some situations (Box 3.4). The design infiltration rate needs to be chosen with these factors in mind, along with the likelihood that maintenance will be undertaken.

Box 3.4   *Surface infiltration rates*

Box 3.4

The infiltration rate of pervious surfaces may be very high when first installed (Table 3.4).

Table 3.4   *Surface infiltration rates*

Reference	Location	Infiltration rate
CIRIA, 1995	Nottingham (Gill Street)	Permeable concrete blocks 1000 mm/h when new 100 mm/h after six years – no maintenance
CIRIA, 1995	Nottingham (Clifton)	Porous asphalt – 10 mm gap graded aggregate 39 000 mm/h mean value after 4.5 years – no maintenance
CIRIA, 1995	Reading, Shire Hall	1700 mm/h to 3600 mm/h (mean of five tests, 2600 mm/h) – no maintenance over five years
Abbott *et al*, 2000	Wheatley (M40) motorway service station	Porous blocks – mean infiltration rate of 1080 mm/h reducing to zero over 10 months Gaps between blocks – mean rate of 51 000 mm/h, after 10 months mean rate of 130 000 mm/h
Abbott *et al*, 2000	Bognor Regis Sports Centre	Porous blocks – mean infiltration rate of 550 mm/h Gaps between the blocks – mean rate of 27 000 mm/h
Bond *et al*, 1999	Laboratory tests	Permeable block surface – 4500 mm/h
CIRIA, 2001	n/a	Quoted figures as general design values Permeable concrete blocks – 4500 mm/h Porous macadam – 10 000 mm/h Concrete grass paviours – >50 mm/h Gravel - > 5000 mm/h
Smith, 2001	Various different locations	New permeable block suface – 229 mm/h Two-year-old car park permeable block – 152 mm/h Four-year-old car park permeable block – 75 mm/h Five-year-old car park permeable block – 127 mm/h

Deposits of silt, litter and the like on the pervious surface need not significantly reduce the surface infiltration rates unless they are compacted into the infiltration void or space by pedestrian or vehicle loading. The maintenance of the surface infiltration rate is best protected by the use of surfaces that do not allow debris to be compacted into the inlets or voids in the surfacing through which rainwater flows. Alternatively, regular sweeping and surface cleaning is required to remove debris. Much of the evidence indicates that a significant factor in whether a pavement clogs is the presence of adjacent landscaping.

American and German experience with permeable concrete block surfacing recommends that the design infiltration rate should be 10 per cent of the initial rate to allow for clogging over a 20-year life (Smith, 2001). Studies in Japan, Germany and France reported by Abbott *et al* (2000) suggest that infiltration rates for pervious pavements decrease by 80–90 per cent over the first one to three years of operation. Design of pervious pavements should take account of these reductions in infiltration capacity.

Shackel (1995) reported tests undertaken on block paving with different combinations of bedding, jointing and drainage cell material. The results showed the highest infiltration capacity of 216 mm/h was obtained with 2–5 mm clean gravel. Rollings and Rollings (1993) found that adding sand to the drainage material significantly reduces infiltration rates.

continued on next page...

Box 3.4 *Surface infiltration rates continued*

Even when the pervious surface remains free-draining, the infiltration rate may be limited by sub-surface elements within the construction, such as a geotextile layer. Where a geotextile filter layer underlies a 50 mm gravel bedding layer, the geotextile will accumulate silts and oils, thus reducing the throughflow considerably compared with the surface infiltration rate (Pratt, 1999). A laboratory study (Schofield, 1994) showed that some 600 g/m² of silts derived from gulley pot liquors would reduce the flow rate through a geotextile (130 g/m² non-woven heat-bonded continuous filament) to 2 mm/h. This significant flow reduction does not necessarily lead to problems at the pervious surface. The 50 mm gravel layer may be assumed to have 30 per cent voids, hence some 15 mm rainfall will be held within the gravel above the geotextile. Table 3.5 shows how this "blockage" still satisfactorily accommodates storm events in excess of a five-year return (for lowland England) (Schofield, 1994). The nature of the geotextile selected will affect this result, as will the nature of the sediment and its supply. It has been shown (Schofield, 1994) that use of a geotextile with increased mass per unit area increases sediment trapping. Higher suspended solids concentrations in the percolating waters and greater deposition on the geotextile also both lead to increased sediment trapping efficiency.

Examination of the geotextile layer at the Nottingham Trent University car park after 18 months of use indicated that the sediment concentration had reached 46 g/m², compared with the 600 g/m² suggested from the laboratory tests.

This investigation identified three alternative modes of failure. Sediment might be transported through the permeable surface to clog the geotextile, or generally fill the gravel layer to restrict throughflow, or it might accumulate in the inlets in the surface, causing blockage, which prevented surface infiltration.

Table 3.5 *Performance of a permeable pavement when the internal geotextile layer below the block paving reduces the throughflow to 2 mm/h (Bond et al, 1999)*

Rainfall duration (minutes/hours)	Total rainfall (mm)	Mean rainfall intensity (mm/h)	Return period of event
15 minutes	15.5	62	>10
30 minutes	16	32	10
1 hour	17	17	3
4 hours	19	4.8	1
10 hours	35	3.5	2
24 hours	63	2.6	5
48 hours	111	2.3	>50

A degree of short-term standing water on some localised areas of pervious surfacing is not typically a problem. Often the entire surface will have a far higher average infiltration capacity than required, so standing waters in some blocked areas will simply flow into adjacent parts of the construction.

An important consideration with pervious surfaces is that soil, sand and other site materials should be prevented from contaminating the pervious surface during construction, thus reducing its free-draining nature. Cahill (2000) suggests that most clogging of pervious surfaces (particularly porous asphalt) occurs during construction. This can be overcome by educating contractors and workers and explaining how the pervious surface works and the importance of keeping it clean. Construction traffic should be prevented from tracking mud and soil into the pervious surface and proper supervision and inspection of the installation should be budgeted into all projects.

After actual construction works cease the preparation of landscaping should be carefully designed and managed to prevent carelessly deposited top soil, turf and other materials blocking the pervious surface. Runoff from landscaped areas, which is a sources of soil and debris, should be prevented from flowing onto the pervious surface and causing clogging.

3.2.2   Internal water movement and storage

Water movement (flow rate and volume) within the pervious construction is determined by the materials used. Materials may range from mixtures of widely ranging particle sizes (continuously graded) to closely graded, near-single-sized (single size grading). Continuously graded soils tend to be more densely packed as the smaller particles fill in the voids; they are stiffer but less permeable. Conversely, single-sized materials with a limited range of sizes have relatively large open voids, which provides a higher permeability and greater storage but are less dense. This is demonstrated in Table 3.6. It has been found that lower densities generally imply lower stiffness.

Table 3.6   *Grading envelopes, density and permeability of graded aggregates (Moulton, 1980)*

% passing by mass		Sample 1	Sample 2	Sample 3	Sample 4	Sample 5	Sample 6
US sieve	Nearest UK						
¼ inch	20 mm	100	100	100	100	100	100
½ inch	14 mm	85	84	83	81.5	79.5	75
³/₈ inch	10 mm	77.5	76	74	72.5	69.5	63
No 4	5 mm	58.5	56	52.5	49	43.5	32
No 8	3.35 mm	42.5	39	34	29.5	22	5.8
No 10	2 mm	39	35	30	25	17	0
No 20	600 micron	26.5	22	15.5	9.8	0	0
No 40	425 micron	18.5	13.3	6.3	0	0	0
No 60	212 micron	13	7.5	0	0	0	0
No 140	150 micron	6	0	0	0	0	0
No 200	75 micron	0	0	0	0	0	0
Dry density	Mg/m³	1.9	1.84	1.81	1.74	1.63	1.59
Permeability	m/s	3.5×10^{-5}	3.8×10^{-4}	1.1×10^{-3}	3.5×10^{-3}	9.2×10^{-3}	1.1×10^{-2}

Note: UK sieve sizes are to be harmonised with a CEN sieve set in the forthcoming BS EN 13043, *Aggregates for bituminous mixtures and surface dressings for roads, airfields and other trafficked areas.*

For pervious pavements, the underlying sub-base should be single-sized so as to facilitate water movement. Organic material should generally be avoided within the construction, but it has been used in temporary, low-budget and/or low-amenity-value situations. Organic materials and continuously graded particle mixtures, with limited voids, will retain moisture, making them susceptible to frost heave if saturated.

The rate of movement of water through a pervious structure depends upon the internal materials. In structures formed from fine, continuously graded material, such as sands, waters will percolate slowly, filling the void spaces and wetting internal surfaces progressively as the waters move downwards. Where the structure contains unbound aggregates with high voids content, the water movement may be rapid without all surfaces being wetted as the flow moves downward. Important considerations are listed below.

- Initial flow is via aggregate-aggregate contact, which results in some surface wetting of aggregates and internal retention, which is dependent upon the surface characteristics of the material.

- The retained water may form droplets/pools at contact points, which are released when a certain size is exceeded, with the result that the volume of water released from the pervious structure may be a function of water storage from a previous rainfall event as well as the current one.

- Full surface wetting of internal material (equivalent of the filling of depression storage) may take a long time, even during the full rainfall duration. Time delay before first discharge from pervious construction is an important benefit in reducing downstream flood risk, where construction discharges to a drainage system. Additionally, surface wetting reduces the volume available for discharge (Box 3.5).

- Where the internal waters discharge through the base of the construction to groundwater, the rate of infiltration of the underlying soil may be a controlling factor on the volume of water retained, temporarily. This soil infiltration rate is far less important than the pervious surface infiltration rate. Internal storage volume within the construction should be designed to be adequate for purpose (Box 3.6 and Box 3.7). The time frame for discharge is a different order to that of traditional surfaces and constructions – typically two or three days, as shown in Figure 3.5. The detention of waters within the structure will have to be considered when reviewing the suitability of construction materials. A high-level overflow from the construction can prevent surface flooding and release excess water safely, if required. The depth of construction is often determined by structural considerations. This depth usually results in adequate hydraulic capacity for internal water storage during storm events or during infiltration through the base of the construction. For example, a typical small-element concrete block surface car park construction about 400 mm deep will hold some 100 litres per square metre of surface area, or 10 mm rainfall.

Box 3.5 *Internal storage, losses and attenuation*

It has been reported (Bond *et al*, 1999) that a permeable pavement laboratory rig had discharges ranging from 47 per cent to 138 per cent (mean 89 per cent) of the rainfall. The outflows varied between lower than predicted and higher than predicted and appeared to oscillate from one to the other. Evidence of this was also reported from observations at the Wheatley (M40) motorway service area (Abbott *et al*, 2000), see Table 3.7 and Case Study No 5 in Appendix 1.

Table 3.7 *Rainfall outflow and observations from Wheatley*

Event	Rainfall duration (hours)	Total rain (mm)	Duration of discharge (days)	Percentage of discharge during rainfall	Percentage of discharge to total rainfall
R16	3.5	4.4	2.28	10.47	82.06
R17	2.42	5.8	3.03	25.06	112.17
R18	6.83	7.6	2.53	15.17	55.77
R19	6.58	11.6	3.75	45.14	120.09
R20	10.83	9.4	3.2	26.86	78.07

Small-element precast concrete blocks have been measured to absorb 4 mm to 5 mm rainfall, with the greatest absorption during long storm events (Mantle, 1993). Observations over 190 days between mid-August and mid-February 1988/89 found that 0.2–5.5 mm of stored water was lost via evaporation. Interestingly, the peak evaporation rates were found to occur in the winter period. The overall mean evaporative loss was 1.1 mm/day. This is significant as it represents an annual loss of some 400 mm, as compared with the mean annual rainfall of 750 mm (Mantle, 1993).

Figure 3.1 shows the effect of these various methods of retention and losses on the runoff from pervious surfaces. The scatter in the diagram for the porous concrete block-surfaced car park shows that there is not the clear linear relationship between runoff and rainfall as shown for the impermeable surface. For the pervious pavement surface the antecedent conditions affect the runoff for each event. Since the moisture content of the pavement changes continuously, the potential runoff from an event is also changing over time. This means that prediction of outflow volumes and rates should be based on a continuous model of pervious pavement moisture content. However, use of the values of initial loss and runoff coefficient given in Box 3.1 provide an adequate basis for constructing an approximate rainfall-runoff model.

Box 3.6 *Assessment of internal storage capacity*

The storage volume in a dry single-sized aggregate can be calculated using the following equation

$$V = 1 - \left(\frac{\gamma_d}{G_s \, \gamma_w} \right) . h$$

Where:
V = maximum storage volume for water below 1 m^2 of surface area (m^3)
γ_d = dry unit weight of soil or aggregate (kN/m^3)
G_s = Specific gravity of soil or aggregate
γ_w = unit weight of water (kN/m^3)
h = thickness of aggregate layer

This equation can only be used for open-graded and dry aggregate as it assumes the degree of saturation is zero.

Box 3.6

3.2.3   Mechanisms involved in outflow/hydrograph attenuation

Wetting losses. The wetting of the pervious surface and the internal materials leads to retention of rainwater, some of which subsequently evaporates. The evaporation of retained water from the granular layers in a small-element, precast concrete block pavement has also been shown to be significant (Box 3.5).

Percolation. Once waters are flowing through a free-draining, granular, sub-structure the velocity of flow downward under gravity is rapid to the base of the construction. Where outflow is to groundwater, the continued downward flow is restricted by the soil infiltration rate. Where construction is underlain by an impermeable geomembrane, lateral flow will be affected by the magnitude of the subgrade surface gradient. This need not be more than 1–2 per cent, as there is no advantage, and possibly some disadvantage, to the rapid release of waters through an increased gradient. If the subgrade gradient is limited, the depth of construction may vary across the width and avoiding excessive depth of construction will be important. Where the general ground gradient exceeds 1–2 per cent, the construction may be built with constant thickness of materials and the subgrade gradient will reflect the pervious surface gradient. Where the subgrade gradient exceeds 5 per cent internal partitions should be installed along the contours, so that flow is downslope via several cross-slope diversions.

Outflow control and internal storage. The subgrade infiltration rate may require storage of excess inflow over outflow, or restrictions on permitted outflow from a pervious structure to a receiving drainage system may demand internal storage capacity. The Environment Agency often requires a maximum permitted discharge of around 5 l/s per impermeable hectare, which may be established by one of a number of flow control systems, but it also can be achieved through the internal attenuation of flow within the pervious structure. For instance, the uncontrolled outflow from the permeable surface car park at Wheatley (M40) motorway service area (case study in Appendix A1) was below 0.4 l/s/ha for 90 per cent of the study time between December 1998 and January 2000 (Abbott *et al*, 2000).

The available internal storage volume should be carefully assessed (Boxes 3.6 and 3.7) particularly where the subgrade is sloping. There is a major advantage to horizontal pervious constructions, as the available storage is then the full rectangular cross-section of the structure. Where the subgrade is sloping, a wedge storage volume is available and care is needed to ensure that waters do not rise in depth within the downstream end of the wedge in order to avoid surface flooding. The internal storage allows for the imposition of any necessary outflow control, thus dictating the form of the hydrograph.

Box 3.7   *Calculation of internal storage volume*

The internal storage volume and thus thickness (based on hydraulic considerations – structural design is also required) is calculated from consideration of the steady-state mass balance of inflow to and outflow from the pavement. For a pervious pavement system that allows infiltration out of the base, the method of determining the required storage volume for plane infiltration systems given in CIRIA Report 156 (Bettess, 1996) may be used. For systems with a piped outlet there is insufficient information available to model accurately the internal flow and storage properties within the sub-base and therefore no allowance should be made for any outflow during the storm, when calculating storage volume of systems with piped outflows.

The required input parameters (Figure 3.7) for infiltration systems are:

q = infiltration coefficient from percolation tests (m/h) – determined following procedure in CIRIA Report 156

A_d = total area to be drained including any adjacent impermeable areas (m²) = $A_I + A_p$

n = porosity of sub-base material (voids volume/total volume)

i = rainfall intensity (m/h)

D = rainfall duration (h)

A_b = base area of infiltration system below pervious pavement (m²)

For internal storage the maximum depth of water that will occur in the sub-base, h_{max}, is based on:

$$h_{max} = D/n.(Ri - q)$$

where R = ratio of drained area to base area of pervious surface, A_d/A_b

The calculation is carried out for a range of rainfall durations to determine the maximum value of h_{max}. This is then the required thickness of sub-base for storage, $h = h_{max}$. (Note traffic requirements and resistance to freezing will also need to be taken into account).

For piped outflows the calculation is simplified to:

$$h_{max} = D/n.(Ri)$$

and is simply carried out for the required return period and storm duration.

Use of single-size unbound aggregates (> 2.5 mm) with high voids content will hold water internally. The storage volume should be increased by 30 per cent to allow any ice formed in cold conditions to expand into the free space without disturbing the structure (Section 4.13).

A worked example is provided in CIRIA Report 156 (Bettess, 1996).

3.2.4   Modelling hydraulic performance

A model of hydraulic performance will comprise four components in a given rainfall regime.

1. Antecedent conditions at the pervious structure (dry period evaporation and outflow).

2. Surface inflow characteristics.

3. Internal storage available.

4. Outflow characteristics.

Antecedent conditions. The design should be conservatively based on storage of the design storm and limiting flows at the outlet to those permitted by regulators.

It should be noted that, presently, there is little basis for prediction of initial conditions at a pervious structure as a result of previous rainfall events and inter-event evaporation and outflows. Since the hydrograph is significantly influenced by these parameters, the accurate prediction of single, specific-event hydrographs is not possible. Pratt *et al* (1995) reported multiple regression equations for predicting the runoff volume and duration of the runoff at a permeable concrete block surface car park in Nottingham. This limited information does not yet allow the initial conditions for a model for the hydrograph at a pervious surface to be established (Pratt *et al*, 1995). While in practice, this can be ignored, these effects will improve design assumptions. As more knowledge is gained the design process may be refined to reduce over-design.

Surface inflow characteristics. For the chosen surfacing material, the design surface infiltration rate must be compared with design rainfall intensities to identify the depth of storage required below the pavement. Where additional areas contribute to the inflow these will need to be modelled to establish a design inflow hydrograph. The design value of surface infiltration rate must be chosen carefully, allowing for the long-term reduction in permeability of pervious pavements, design life and acceptability of ponding (Box 3.4). The design infiltration rate should take account of all the layers of the system, including for example the permeability of infill between paving blocks. A conservative value should be adopted.

Internal storage volume required. In conjunction with structural design considerations, the required internal storage volume should be assessed taking account of the outflow method (via base or a drainage outlet). The aim of this component of the modelling is to identify the maximum depth of internal water storage and to be assured that it is safely contained within the construction.

The storage volume required below the pavement can be estimated in a simplistic manner. For outflow into the underlying ground the method described in CIRIA Report 156 (Bettess, 1996) for plane infiltration systems can be used (See Box 3.7). Additional information is provided by Smith (2001). More complex methods are proposed by the United States Environmental Protection Agency (USEPA, 1980). These require the use of the computer program PORPAVE to be used in everyday design and are not justified at this stage given the uncertainties in knowledge of water storage and movement mechanisms within pervious pavements.

For general situations the pavement should be designed to store water for the design rainfall event. They should empty from full to half empty within 24–48 hours in readiness to accept subsequent storm inflow, but without exceeding the discharge limits. This will also minimise the amount of time the subgrade is exposed to traffic loads when saturated, if an impermeable geomembrane is not used.

It is not possible to accurately model the wetting losses and the length of time to first release of water from drainage pipes, in the case of undersealed constructions. Macdonald and Jefferies (2001) have established a relationship between the lag time before first discharge and the previous five-day rainfall for a permeable-surface car park in Edinburgh. At present, modelling will likely give the worse-case hydrograph, such that first flows are predicted too early and outflow volume is over-estimated (Macdonald and Jefferies, 2001).

For outflow into pipes the time to empty the storage volume through the pipes is based on two factors.

1. The capacity of the pipes, which depends on gradient, diameter and roughness of the pipe walls. This can be determined using established procedures for conventional drainage.

2. The horizontal transmissivity of the sub-base, which depends on permeability, thickness, gradient and hydraulic gradient to the pipe. A method of calculation is given by Cao *et al* (1998).

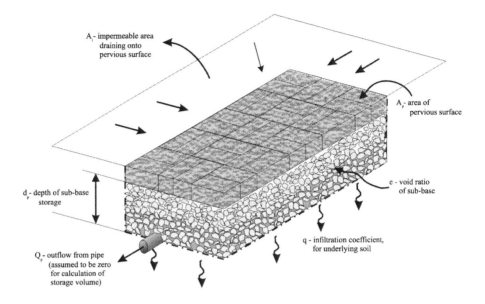

Figure 3.7   *Design parameters for calculating the storage depth of pervious pavements*

Outflow characteristics. The mode of release of the waters from the construction will determine these. To avoid the need to analyse outflow characteristics, pervious pavements should be designed to store the volume of water from the design storm. The outflow of water can then be determined by assessing infiltration rates and/or choice of pipe sizes and gradients to achieve the required maximum permitted outlet flows and emptying times. This will give a conservative estimate of the outflow hydrograph (higher peak flows than will occur in practice). If infiltration is used, the soil infiltration rates must be determined from site tests (Bettess, 1996).

The flow chart in Figure 3.8 illustrates the modelling process assuming the site is suitable for pervious surfacing to be used (Box 5.2). Antecedent conditions must be ignored until a continuous model of internal moisture can be constructed for the pervious surface, accounting for evaporation and discharge during dry periods.

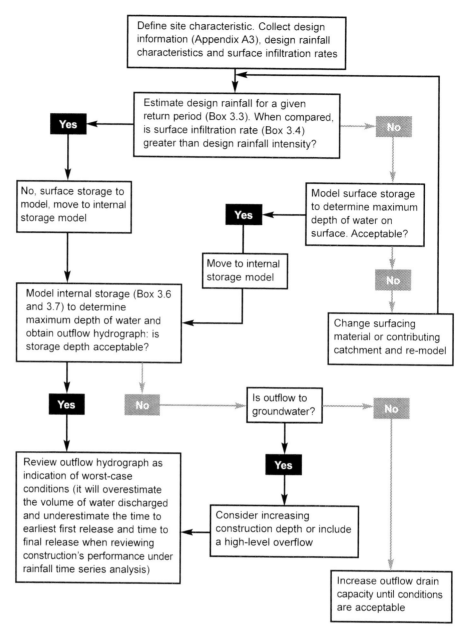

Figure 3.8   *Flow chart of hydraulic modelling*

See Box 6.1 for recommended design flow chart for overall design of pervious pavements.

3.3   MAINTENANCE

3.3.1   Routine maintenance requirements

The maintenance requirements of a pervious surface should be reviewed at the time of design and be clearly specified. Maintenance is required to prevent clogging of the pervious surface (see Section 3.2.1 and Box 3.4). This may vary from occasional cutting of grass within a grass protection system, for convenience, to daily vacuum-sweeping at a supermarket, as part of a company's environmental image.

The factors to be considered when defining maintenance requirements include:

- type of use (maintenance will need to be intensified as public use grows and as litter/debris increases)

- access to the surface – is it open to the public or is it private?

- the level of trafficking – volume of traffic, axle loads and vehicle speeds
- the local environment – for example, is the area established or are building works being conducted locally?
- the proximity and nature of landscaping and gardens – for example, will there be loose soil/plant debris from gardening activities or seasonal leaf fall?
- long-term ownership and responsibility for the surface
- responsibility for maintenance – will the owner or users undertake this and should they be advised to do so?

Cahill (2000) recommends that pervious surfaces are vacuum-cleaned twice a year using commercially available sweeping machines; site owners should also be given a checklist of the monitoring and maintenance requirements (see Appendix A4). UK experience is limited, but advice issued with permeable precast concrete paving in public locations has been for a minimum of three surface sweepings a year:

- end of winter (April)
- mid-summer (July/August) to collect flower and grass-type deposits
- after autumn leaf fall (November).

Such a recommendation includes only environmental considerations and would need to be amended in the light of change in public usage, for example Saturday markets. However, the infiltration rates of most pervious surfaces are so much greater than rainfall intensity that even when left unmaintained the infiltration rate of pervious surfacing may still be sufficient to allow infiltration of the design rainfall events, especially if reduction in infiltration rates has been allowed for in design (Box 3.4).

As with traditional non-pervious pavements, the general recommendation on maintenance must be to keep the trafficked surface free from debris at whatever frequency of operation that demands. Debris collecting on the surface in areas where it is not crushed into the surface will not inhibit infiltration, so its removal may be delayed until convenient.

An important consideration to prevent clogging is to ensure that mud and debris are not allowed to be tracked onto the surface during construction (see Section 3.2.1).

Long-term maintenance also needs to be considered when deriving whole-life costings (see Appendix A5).

Laboratory research data and field monitoring of long-term performance has been encouraging in predicting that life-spans of 20-plus trouble-free years can occur (Wei, 1985; Smith, 2001; Rommel *et al*, 2001). Where clogging has occurred in many instances it appears to be due to runoff carrying soil from adjacent landscaping areas (see case study for M40 MSA in Appendix A1, Section 3.2.1 and Box3.4).

Laboratory results are not necessarily a true reflection of field performance, because they cannot model airborne deposition on the pervious surface and its effect. Estimation of the effect of oiling of a permeable surface and of the underlying geotextile layer are that it is of limited significance so long as the quantity of oil is controlled and dispersed in time (Pratt, 1999).

Kipkie (1998) reported testing on a permeable block pavement in Canada before and after cleaning with a vacuum street sweeper. The pavement had been in service for three years and the sweeping increased the average infiltration rate from 3.6 mm/h to 5 mm/h.

3.3.2   Remedial maintenance requirements

Inadequate maintenance will almost certainly become evident through standing water remaining on the pervious surface for unacceptably long periods. If cleaning does not restore infiltration rates then reconstruction of part or the whole of a pervious surface may be required. This process should be considered during design and specification of the pavement. The time before this becomes necessary can be roughly estimated by considering the factor of safety applied to the surface infiltration rate (Box 3.4) and the estimated time for the underlying layers to reach their maximum adsorption capacity for contaminants (Section 5.4.2 and 5.4.3). Hydraulic failure will require the affected surface area being lifted for inspection of the internal materials to identify the location and extent of the blockage. Smith (2001) also recommends installing inspection wells into the sub-base layers to monitor performance and give advance warnings of any potential problems.

With modular or small element permeable block paving and grass/gravel protection systems, the surfacing material may be lifted and reused after brush cleaning: the layers below the surface and material infilling the surface voids will need cleaning or replacing, but new materials (and hence costs) may be limited. Materials removed from the voids or the layers below the surface may contain heavy metals and hydrocarbons (as is the case with asphalt surfacing) and need to be disposed as a controlled waste. This is no more onerous than the disposal of gully pot or interceptor sediments. The applicable legislation is discussed in Box 3.8.

Box 3.8   *Waste disposal of sediments*

Under the Controlled Waste Regulations 1992, the sediments removed from below a pervious surface will be regarded as industrial, and therefore controlled, waste (as is the case with liquid or sediment removed from conventional gullies). This places duties on the owner of the pervious surface to dispose of the material in accordance with the relevant legislation.

Legislation to note includes:

Environmental Protection Act, 1990 – introduced the statutory duty of care in relation to waste and provides a definition of waste.

Environmental Protection (Duty of Care) Regulations, 1991 – place a statutory duty of care upon anyone who produces or disposes of controlled waste, or as a broker, has control of such waste. The practical implications are that waste sediment must be removed by a registered haulier to a registered waste disposal site, that is licensed to accept such materials. The waste must be accompanied by a consignment note that accurately describes the waste and the volumes being removed.

Waste Management Licensing Regulations, 1994 – provides a definition of waste.

Special Waste Regulations, 1996 – these define special waste on a hazard basis. The practical implications are that only certain landfill or treatment sites are licensed to accept special waste and the Environment Agency must be notified in advance of any material being removed to the disposal site. Consignment notes are used to track special waste from source to disposal.

Special Waste Regulations (NI), 1998 – these apply to the disposal of special waste in Northern Ireland.

Waste sediment is subject to landfill tax, under the *Landfill Tax Regulations*, 1996, at the prevailing rate if it is removed to landfill.

The hydraulic performance of continuous-laid permeable surfacing may be reinstated by renewal of the infill material. The ability to empty and recharge the voids makes this surfacing maintainable with limited disruption of its use. Again, disposal of any void-filling materials must be conducted with regard to it potentially being contaminated (see Box 3.8). The effectiveness of this procedure depends upon the depth of penetration of blockage materials below the surface and the degree of compaction by traffic.

When porous surfacing needs replacing, typically there will be considerably higher costs associated with the process, as none of the surfacing to be renewed can be reused without being taken off site for processing. Some porous materials tend to block within the surface and are not capable of effective cleaning. Experience in Sweden and France has shown that initially significant improvement in the infiltration rate of porous asphalt/concrete can be achieved, but the level of improvement decreases rapidly with each event (Skrettegerg, 1990). Eventually all the affected surface material must be removed and re-laid. The surface tends to filter the blocking material and retain it, so there is not likely to be a need for further material replacement below the surface. Again, care will be required in disposing of the surfacing material as blockages are likely to be contaminated with heavy metals and hydrocarbons when the surface has been used by vehicles (see Box 3.8). Reconstruction works will disrupt the use of the affected area.

Typically, the reconstruction of small element block surfaces is likely to be less costly and disruptive than that of continuous concrete or asphalt porous surfaces.

4   Structural performance issues

4.1   PAVEMENT DESIGN METHODS

There are three elements to be considered in the structural design of vehicular trafficked pervious surfaces.

1. The surface course (porous asphalt, concrete slab, concrete blocks, reinforced gravel or grass). The function of the surface material is to provide a good quality ride combined with appropriate skid resistance and resistance to crack propagation in the bituminous and concrete surfaces. Texture and durability under trafficking are key considerations.

2. The underlying construction layers that spread the applied loads (binder course, base, concrete slab and sub-base). These layers are required to provide a stable construction platform and spread the applied construction and traffic loading so that the underlying foundation layers are not over-stressed.

3. The foundation soils (capping layer and subgrade). This is the platform upon which the structural layers are placed.

The layers that are present in conventional bituminous, block paving and concrete surfaces are shown in Figure 4.1. In pervious surface construction the surfacing layers are pervious to allow water to pass through to the underlying foundation (sub-base and capping layers) where it is stored before discharge.

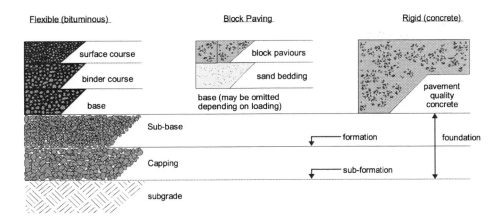

CEN definitions for pavement layers used – see Table 1.1

Figure 4.1   *Diagram of conventional pavement layers (Highways Agency et al, 1992)*

The design of each layer of the pavement is determined by the likely traffic loadings (Box 4.1) and its required operational life. Current UK practice for pavement design has developed on the basis of practical experience combined with laboratory research and monitoring the performance of constructed roads. The methods are summarised in Box 4.2.

Box 4.1 *Traffic loading*

> The maximum loads imposed on road and car park pavements are those from commercial vehicles, heavy goods vehicles (including refuse-collection lorries), buses and coaches. Pavements are designed to carry a predicted number of goods vehicles throughout their design life, in terms of a standard axle load. This is referred to in terms of million standard axles (msa). In comparison the structural damage caused by lighter traffic is negligible. Guidance on estimating the traffic loads for a pavement is given in the *Design Manual for Roads and Bridges*, HD 24 (Highways Agency *et al*, 1992).
>
> An alternative approach adopted by some design methods is to classify traffic loading based on gross vehicle weight.
>
> The volume of traffic (how many vehicles, regardless of weight) may also be a consideration in respect of maintenance of pervious surfaces.

There is no current structural design method in the UK specifically for pervious pavements. They have, however, been in service in car parks in the USA for over 20 years and are used widely in Germany for applications such as bus and lorry parks, where heavy axle loads occur. Adverse structural effects have not been reported.

One particular demonstration project was constructed at Walden Ponds State Reservation in Massachusetts, USA. This was undertaken as part of a 1972 US Environmental Protection Agency demonstration project and was well monitored and documented (Wei, 1986). The trial section comprised porous asphalt (63 mm thick) over 300 mm of open-graded aggregate. There have been no adverse structural effects reported.

The conventional pavement design methods described in Box 4.2 and the analytical techniques described in Figure 4.2 can be used for the design of pervious pavements. The key to successful structural design and performance is to recognise the difference between pervious and conventional pavements and make due allowances for the following factors in the design and specification of materials:

- pervious pavements use materials with high permeability and void space. All the current structural pavement design methods commonly used in the UK are based on the use of conventional materials (which are dense and relatively impermeable). The stiffness of the materials to be used must, therefore, be assessed. This can be done based on equivalence (Section 4.12)

- water is present within the construction and can soften and weaken materials and this must be allowed for (Section 4.4)

- pavement designers should satisfy themselves that the materials to be used do not invalidate the assumptions made in the structural design methods (Box 4.2)

- the design methods assume full friction between layers. Any geotextiles or geomembranes must be carefully specified to minimise loss of friction between layers (Section 4.8 and 4.9)

- porous asphalt loses adhesion (binder stripping) and becomes brittle as air passes through the voids. Its durability is therefore lower than conventional materials (Section 4.6.1)

- the single-sized grading of the materials used means care must be taken to ensure that loss of finer particles between unbound layers does not occur (Box 4.4 and Section 6.4.1).

Box 4.2   *Design methods*

Three approaches to conventional pavement design are commonly used by engineers in the UK. The groupings used are simplified for the purposes of this book and the precise classification of roads is provided in the Highways Act 1980 – see CIRIA Report 142 (Luker and Montague, 1994). All the methods for flexible pavement design are based on the same philosophy but with a greater or lesser degree of simplification, depending on the circumstances.

Situation	Design method
Motorways trunk and other high speed roads	Structural design of pavements for motorways, trunk roads and other major highways is undertaken using the guidance provided in the *Design Manual for Roads and Bridges* (Highways Agency *et al*, 1992). They are constructed using either flexible or rigid pavement materials (bituminous or concrete respectively). The relevant section is *Volume 7, Pavement Design and Maintenance*, which is a series of linked documents.
	Design Manual for Roads and Bridges. Volume 7
	The relevant sections for structural pavement design are *HD23 – General information* *HD24 – Traffic assessment* *HD25 – Foundations* *HD26 – Pavement design* *HD36 – Surfacing materials for new and maintenance construction* *HD37 – Bituminous surfacing materials and techniques*
	The basic method of design follows that described in TRRL Report LR1132 (Powell *et al*, 1984) and Research Report 87 (Mayhew and Harding, 1987). The method relates the traffic loading and subgrade strength to the required thickness of the sub-base and structural bituminous layers, using a series of graphs, and relies on practical experience of the performance of conventional materials used in bituminous or concrete roads. The latest amendment to HD26 (August 2001) also allows analytical design methods to be used (see Box 4.2), but regard must be given to the overall strength, durability and ease of maintenance of the pavement.
Block paving	Car parks, docks, warehouse hardstandings and similar areas may use block paving. Block paving is designed using BS 7533-1:2001 and for lightly trafficked areas using BS 7533-2:2001. Part 1 of the standard uses a similar approach to the DMRB and relates CBR, traffic volumes and the size of a development to the required construction thickness. The second part of the standard relates the type of use of a pavement to the CBR value of the sub-grade to give required pavement layer thickness. Concrete block manufacturers have also developed a design method for pervious block pavements (Knapton, 2002). For lightly trafficked areas where limited numbers of commercial vehicles are allowed gravel or grass reinforcement may be used. This is usually designed using manufacturer's design guides.

continued on next page...

Box 4.2   *Design methods (cont)*

	Design method
Estate roads, distributor roads, residential roads and car parks	Design is usually based on prescriptive descriptions provided by the adopting authority, based on the type of construction and road use. These may also include custom material specifications based on knowledge of the behaviour of locally available materials . Flexible and rigid pavements may be designed using the semi-quantitative methods in the *Design Manual for Roads and Bridges* (DMRB) or using the guidance provided in Transport Research Laboratory Reports LR1132 or RR87.
	Example of a local authority specification <u>***Shared surface construction for access ways/access court and mews court.***</u> *Rectangular interlocking concrete block paving, 60 mm thick* *Concrete blocks laid on a screeded layer over 35 mm compacted thickness of naturally occurring sand complying with BS 7533: Part 3. Method of laying to be in accordance with BS 6717: Part 3. Other types of block paving may be approved on request* *Base course, 50 mm thick* *20 mm size dense basecourse complying with South Yorkshire Laboratory Specification No 31 and BS 4987* *Sub-base in accordance with CBR value of subgrade. 340 mm to be laid unless site investigation indicates a lesser thickness will suffice*
	Note this is a summary of the specification for illustration purposes only. From *General Specification for Roads to be Adopted as Public Highways*, Sheffield Metropolitan District Council, Planning, Transport and Highways, Adoptions Group, November 1998.
Abnormally heavy loaded areas (eg ports, airports, etc)	Pavement areas subjected to abnormally heavy loads, such as port container depots and airports, need special consideration and are usually designed using specific guidance related to the application. One example is the British Ports Federation (Knapton and Meletiou, 1996) design manual, which used finite element analysis to develop design charts for concrete block paving. This could be used for all types of pervious pavements providing the elastic modulus and Poisson's ratio are known.
Overseas design methods	In the USA structural design of permeable block paving is generally undertaken in accordance with the design guide produced by the Interlocking Concrete Pavement Institute (Smith, 2001). The method of design is not stated and the pavement thickness required for structural purposes is derived from a set of tables, so applicability in the UK is not known.
Other design methods	Some analytical design methods are based on elastic analysis of the soils and pavement layers under loading (see Figure 4.2). These have been developed by, among others, Shell (1985), British Airports Authority (Woodman, 1992), Nottingham University (Brown and Brunton, 1984) and the Australian Government (Austroads, 1992). Computer programmes are available that undertake the calculations required. These rely to a lesser degree on past performance monitoring.

Pavement design in the UK is based to some extent on experience and performance monitoring of existing pavements. There is limited experience of using pervious pavements subject to heavy axle loads in the UK and in these situations design advice from specialist pavement and geotechnical engineers should be sought.

4.2 DESIGN CRITERIA

To provide satisfactory performance a pavement must meet certain structural criteria. The most important of these are listed below:

- the subgrade must be able to sustain traffic loading without excessive deformation
- the granular capping and sub-base layers must give sufficient load spreading to provide an adequate construction platform and base for the overlying pavement layers
- the bituminous, concrete, blocks or other pavement materials must not crack or suffer excessive rutting under the influence of traffic. This is controlled by the horizontal tensile stress at the base of these layers.

Pavements do not usually fail suddenly, but their serviceability tends to reduce gradually, until a terminal level is reached beyond which they cannot be repaired and complete reconstruction is required. TRRL LR1132 (Powell *et al*, 1984) defines the failure of bituminous flexible pavements as the point at which rutting depths are 10 mm or when cracking in the pavement surface occurs. This is normally an indication that significant structural failure is about to occur. A similar definition of failure would apply to block paving surfaces. For concrete pavements rutting does not occur and the onset of cracking in the pavement surface or differential movement at joints greater than 10 mm is defined as failure in TRL RR87 (Mayhew and Harding, 1987).

Most analytical pavement design methods assume that the pavement system is a linear elastic multi-layer model. The materials are characterised by elastic modulus and Poisson's ratio, and are assumed to be homogeneous and isotropic. A simplified pavement structure is illustrated below.

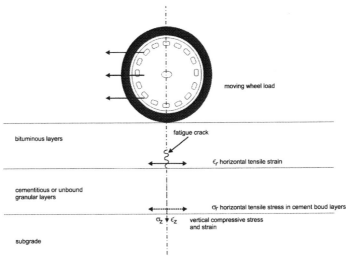

The elastic stresses, strains and vertical deflections are calculated and compared to the sub-grade failure criteria. In each case the failure criteria are an inseparable part of the particular design method and they should not be extracted and used outside the context of that method.

It is important to recognise that all the methods assume complete friction between the layers. This will not be the case if impermeable geomembranes are incorporated into the pavement structure (including between the foundation soils and constructed structure). Care should there-fore be taken in this situation to make sure the methods remain valid. Geotextiles may also have a similar effect.

Figure 4.2 *Analytical structural design methods*

4.3 IMPLICATIONS OF THE STRUCTURAL DESIGN OF CONSTRUCTED PERVIOUS PAVEMENTS

Pervious pavements can be as structurally competent as conventional pavements, providing certain aspects are given careful consideration at the design stage, as discussed in Section 4.1. The single-sized nature of the aggregate materials used to create high voids ratios and permeability means that they can be less stiff than continuously graded materials. Porous asphalt is also less stiff than dense bituminous materials (Potter and Halliday, 1981) and ages faster as air comes into contact with the binder and causes embrittlement. Conversely, concrete block paving has a comparable or greater stiffness than dense bituminous materials.

The other major difference between conventional and pervious pavement systems relates to the presence of water. In conventional systems the design attempts to minimise water infiltration through the pavement. However, pavement engineers know that water does get through the surface via cracks in the pavement, infiltration at the edges and through joints in concrete. It is possible that up to 30 per cent of rainfall on a conventional pavement will infiltrate into the sub-base. As a result there is a requirement to remove water from the pavement layers quickly using drainage systems.

For pervious pavements the water is to be held within the pavement layers and may be infiltrated to the underlying soils. The effect of water on the structural performance of the system, and in particular the strength of the pavement sub-base layers and foundation subgrade, needs careful consideration. If this is done they will be less affected than conventional impermeable sub-bases, which can trap water within them.

The impermeable nature of conventional sub-base was demonstrated by Cedergren (1974), who reported that materials with greater than 3 per cent passing the 75 micron sieve were specified to give a permeability less than 5×10^{-6} m/s for use as core material in a dam. This compares to Type 1 sub-base, which can have up to 10 per cent passing the 75 micron sieve (Figure 4.3).

4.4 SUBGRADE

The main issue is the presence of water in the pavement structure causing saturation of the foundation soils, with a resulting loss of strength and stiffness. The severity of the effects depends on the type of soil (Table 4.1).

Table 4.1 *Sensitivity of subgrade strength and stiffness to increased moisture content*

Soil type	Sensitivity
Clay	Very sensitive: small increases in moisture content cause rapid loss of strength and stiffness
Silt	Very sensitive: small increases in moisture content cause rapid loss of strength and stiffness
Chalk	Very sensitive: changes in moisture content cause loss of strength
Fill materials	Moderate to very sensitive, depending on type of soil. (Note – infiltration is not appropriate on loosely consolidated fill due to the risk of collapse compression and an impermeable geomembrane should always be used in this situation)
Granular (sand, gravel)	Low to moderate sensitivity, depending on the proportion of clay and silt present
Rock	Very low to moderate sensitivity. Weak argillaceous rocks (those with a high proportion of clay-sized particles) or highly weathered material will be most susceptible to moisture content changes and saturation. Strong, slightly weathered sandstone and igneous rocks should not be significantly affected under traffic loads

The stiffness modulus and shear strength of the subgrade depend on such factors as plasticity, degree of remoulding, density and effective stress. The effective stress is in turn dependent on the stress caused by the overlying layers, the stress history and the pore water pressure or suction. The number of factors affecting the design stiffness has led to the development of an empirical index test, the California Bearing Ratio (CBR) test, to simplify pavement design.

The CBR is not a direct measure of strength or stiffness but much experience has been gained in its use for pavement design. It is very useful as a comparison of subgrades and is used by many of the design methods discussed previously. The test is described in Box 4.3.

Box 4.3   *Measurement of CBR*

The laboratory measurement of the California Bearing Ratio (CBR) is carried out in accordance with BS 1377: Part 4: 1990. It can also be measured *in situ*, in accordance with BS 1377: Part 9: 1990.

It is an empirical test developed by the California State Highway Association. The CBR value is simply the resistance to a penetration of 2.54 mm of a standard cylindrical plunger of 49.6 mm diameter, expressed as a percentage of the known resistance of the plunger to various penetrations in crushed aggregate (13.4 kN at 2.5 mm and 20.2 kN at 5 mm).

The soil is held in mould of 152 mm diameter and 177 mm depth. It is undertaken on soil with all particles retained on the 20 mm sieve removed. It is not therefore appropriate for soils with a greater particle size as the plunger and aggregate particles will be of similar size. The plunger is pushed into the soil at a rate of 1 mm per minute and the plunger load recorded for each 0.25 mm penetration up to a maximum of 7.5 mm.

The test results are plotted in the form of load penetration graph and the resistance at 2.5 mm is expressed as a percentage of 13.24 kN and at 5 mm as a percentage of 19.96 kN. The higher of the two values is the CBR value.

It does not measure strength or stiffness directly, but gives a combined measure of both. The CBR value for soils with a maximum size greater than 20 mm (such as required in the sub-base and capping layers) can be measured indirectly using the plate bearing test described in BS 1377: Part 9: 1990.

If the CBR value cannot be measured directly it can be estimated from tables provided in DMRB or TRRL Report LR1132 (Powell *et al*, 1984). Where geomembrane containment is not provided, a high water table and poor construction conditions should be assumed, to allow for the effects of water storage in the granular layers. This should allow for the saturation of the subgrade that may occur (Table 4.2).

The measured CBR value of a subgrade can also be used to estimate the stiffness using the following equation from TRL LR1132:

$$E = 17.6 \, (CBR)^{0.64} \ MPa$$

where CBR is in per cent. This is reported to be a lower bound relationship valid between CBR values of 2 per cent and 12 per cent.

The CBR value used in the design of pervious pavement systems should be measured or estimated for the saturated foundation soils, unless an impermeable geomembrane is provided to prevent water infiltration. If it is to be measured directly, CBR samples should be taken and soaked in water in accordance with BS 1377: Part 4: 1990. This should give a good estimation of the performance of the foundation soils under a pervious pavement.

Table 4.2   *Equilibrium CBR values for pervious pavement design (Powell et al, 1984)*

Type of soil	Plasticity index	Thin pavement (300 mm thick)[1]	Thick pavement (1200 mm thick)[1]
Heavy clay[2]	70	1.5 to 2	2
	60	1.5 to 2	2 to 2.5
	50	1.5 to 2	2 to 2.5
	40	2 to 3	2.5 to 3
Silty clay	30	2.5 to 3.5	3.5 to 5
Sandy clay	20	2.5 to 4.5	4 to 7
	10	1.5 to 3.5	3.5 to 7
Silt[2]	—	1	1
Sand (poorly graded)	—	20	20
Sand (well graded)	—	40	40
Sandy gravel (well graded)	—	60	60

Notes

1. For systems where water will be stored in contact with the subgrade or infiltration is required the lower value in a range should be used.

2. A geomembrane should always be provided over silts and high-plasticity clays (plasticity index > 40).

Care should be adopted when designing heavily loaded areas (HGV traffic) on subgrades used for infiltration or where water will be stored without geomembranes. The advice of a chartered civil engineer with geotechnical experience should be sought.

4.5   CAPPING AND SUB-BASE LAYERS

4.5.1   Specification and design

The granular capping layer is provided to improve and protect weak subgrades from damage due to construction traffic by using cheap locally available materials. The capping is provided to increase the stiffness of the formation on to which the sub-base will be placed (minimum CBR value of 15 per cent is usually required). The sub-base provides a stable platform for pavement construction. In a pervious pavement system the capping and sub-base layers must also store and drain infiltrated water, in addition to their structural role.

The sub-base is intended to be a structural layer with a high stiffness. In a conventional pavement it is also meant to be relatively impermeable and to shed water during construction. This requires a continuously graded material with sufficient fines to fill the voids between the larger particles to give good interlock. Figure 4.3 shows the grading for Type 1 sub-base from the *Specification for Highway Works*. In a pervious system there is still a requirement for stiffness, but the material needs both to be permeable to allow water to flow through it and to have sufficient void space for water storage (Section 3.2). The grading of conventional granular Type 1 sub-base (Figure 4.3) is thus not compatible with pervious systems and other materials must be used.

A common misconception with pervious pavements is that the presence of water in the unbound layers reduces their strength and stiffness. Although this is true for materials such as Type 1 sub-base it does not apply to the single-sized materials used in pervious pavements. Type 1 sub-base has a relatively high fines content and is therefore affected by changes in moisture content. The single-sized nature of the sub-base required in a pervious pavement requires a low fines content. Although it will have a lower stiffness than Type 1, it will not be significantly reduced further by the presence of water within it, provided there is sufficient friction between particles when saturated.

Pervious pavements require a single-size grading to give open voids. The choice of materials for use in capping and sub-base layers below pervious pavements is therefore a compromise between stiffness, permeability and storage capacity. Materials within 450 mm of the surface should also be non-frost-susceptible (see Section 4.13.2) unless it is proved they can limit frost penetration to a shallower depth.

American experience of the effect of changes in grading on permeability and density (Moulton, 1980) is shown in Table 3.6.

No specific structural design guidance exists in the UK for the selection of high void capping or sub-base material. The single-sized materials above 2 mm nominal size shown in Figure 4.3 are all acceptable subject to site-specific considerations and testing to confirm they will perform as required.

Any materials used in pervious systems should be tested to confirm the permeability, void space and stiffness before the main construction takes place. If the elastic modulus of the materials is needed in order that analytical design can be carried out, the dynamic effects of vehicle loading must be taken into account when choosing an appropriate test method. Ideally, the dynamic stiffness modulus (which is different to the modulus measured in a plate bearing test) should be determined directly, for example from repeated load triaxial tests.

The guidance provided in Box 4.4 should also be followed to ensure an acceptable grading is obtained with no loss of fines between layers.

Ease of construction also needs to be considered. A uniformly graded single-size material cannot be compacted and is liable to move when construction traffic passes over it. This effect can be reduced by the use of angular crushed rock material with a high surface friction (Box 4.5). Site trials in which test areas are constructed have also proved beneficial in choosing the aggregate that gives the best compromise between constructability and void ratio (see Case Study No 1, Appendix A1).

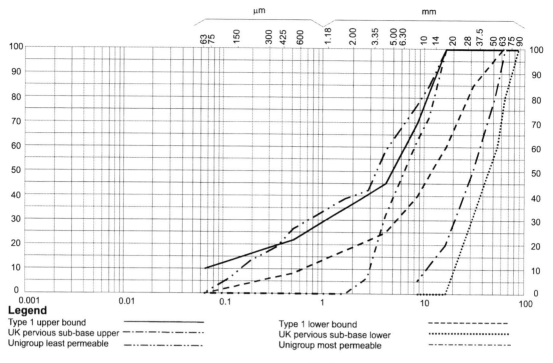

Standard Sieve Sizes

Legend

Type 1 upper bound	Type 1 lower bound
UK pervious sub-base upper	UK pervious sub-base lower
Unigroup least permeable	Unigroup most permeable

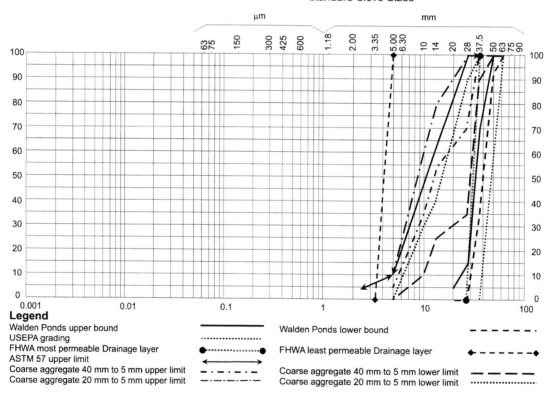

Standard Sieve Sizes

Legend

Walden Ponds upper bound	Walden Ponds lower bound
USEPA grading	
FHWA most permeable Drainage layer	FHWA least permeable Drainage layer
ASTM 57 upper limit	
Coarse aggregate 40 mm to 5 mm upper limit	Coarse aggregate 40 mm to 5 mm lower limit
Coarse aggregate 20 mm to 5 mm upper limit	Coarse aggregate 20 mm to 5 mm lower limit

Figure 4.3   *Grading envelopes*

Box 4.4   *Grading requirements for pervious sub-base and capping layers*

Cedergren (1974) proposed the following criteria for open-graded aggregates used in drainage layers, which are also applicable to the unbound layers in pervious pavement systems:

$4 \, D_{15} > D_{85}$
$D_2 > 2.54 \, mm$

This should ensure that voids are large enough to give reasonable storage and should also avoid the problem of heave due to freeze-thaw.

Design guidance for permeable interlocking concrete pavements in the USA (Smith, 2001) recommends the use of aggregate complying with American Society of Testing Materials (ASTM) No 57 material (ASTM, 2001). This material is then blinded with a "choke aggregate" to give an even surface for the overlying construction. The choke aggregate is specified as ASTM No 8 material and should be no greater than 75 mm thick. To prevent loss of the choke aggregate into the underlying fill, it should meet the following requirements:

$D_{15 \text{ open-graded base}} / D_{50 \text{ choke aggregate}} < 5$
and
$D_{50 \text{ open-graded base}} / D_{50 \text{ choke aggregate}} > 2$.

If a similar approach is adopted in the UK it is possible to use aggregate in accordance with BS 882 (1992). The most appropriate are the 40 mm to 5 mm and 20 mm to 5 mm crushed rock coarse aggregate. The single-size 5 mm aggregate may meet the requirements for a choke aggregate.

Table 4.3   *Grading requirements for ASTM No 57 and No 8 material*

Sieve size mm (nearest UK equivalent)	Percentage passing	
	ASTM No 57	**ASTM No 8**
37.5	100	—
28	95 to 100	—
14	20 to 60	100
10	—	85 to 100
5	0 to 10	10 to 30
2.36	0 to 5	0 to 10
1.18	—	0 to 5

Note: based on ASTM C33 *Specification for concrete aggregates*

Table 4.4   *Recommended grading requirements from BS 882: 1992*

Sieve size mm (nearest UK equivalent)	Percentage passing		
	Coarse aggregate 40 mm to 5 mm	**Coarse aggregate 20 mm to 5 mm**	**Single-size aggregate 5 mm**
50	100	—	—
37.5	90 to 100	100	—
20	35 to 70	90 to 100	—
14	25 to 55	40 to 80	—
10	10 to 40	30 to 60	100
5	0 to 5	0 to 10	45 to 100
2.36	—	—	0 to 30

Note: based on BS 882: 1992 *Specification for aggregates from natural sources for concrete*

Although single-sized materials tend to be less stiff and have higher deflections under load, research by Highlands and Hoffman (1988) indicates that they have a lower degree of stress development, which should reduce rutting.

The DMRB suggests a sub-base with a CBR of 30 per cent, measured in the laboratory, should provide a suitable platform on which to construct the overlying bituminous or concrete layers. There is no reason why this cannot be achieved with materials that are sufficiently permeable for use in pervious pavements. Caution should be applied when undertaking testing to ensure that large pieces of aggregate are not influencing the results of the test. Plate bearing tests on a trial section of material are a more effective way to measure the CBR of more open-graded and coarse materials used as sub-base in pervious systems.

Because the sub-base and capping are also going to be in contact with water for much of the time, the strength and durability of the aggregate particles when saturated and subjected to wetting and drying should assessed. The materials should also not crush or degrade either during construction or in service. The specification of Los Angeles Abrasion test values, 10 per cent fines tests and flakiness tests will address these issues (Box 4.5).

Box 4.5   *Recommended specification of aggregate for strength and durability*

The requirement for low fines content means the load in the sub-base will be carried essentially by point-to-point contact between aggregate particles. To maximise the friction between particles, and thus increase strength, the soil particles should be rough and angular to provide good interlocking between particles. Crushed rock (granite, basalt, gabbro) or concrete with greater than 90 per cent fracture faces or blast furnace slag is required to achieve this, and sand and gravel with rounded particles should not be used in pervious pavement sub-base construction.

Blast furnace slag should comply with British Standard BS 1047: 1983. The presence of contaminants within the slag leaching out into the percolating rainwater should be considered and leaching tests should be undertaken to confirm that this will not occur at significant rates. Leaching tests should be carried out in accordance with either the former National Rivers Authority method (Lewin *et al*, 1994) or the Toxicity Characteristic Leaching Procedure (Federal Register, 1986).

Aggregate for use in the sub-base and/or capping layers below pervious surfaces should also comply with the following requirements.

Los Angeles Abrasion Test. Moisture absorption by soil like rocks (for example, mud aggregate) causes disaggregation in the form of powdering or spalling of the sample surface or separations along bedding planes. These types of materials are unsuitable for use in pervious pavements and the test determines the resistance of rocks to abrasion and drying/wetting. Aggregates for use in pervious pavements should have values of percentage of wear < 25 per cent.

10 per cent fines test. This gives an indication of an aggregate's resistance to crushing. For pervious pavement the test should be carried out on saturated samples. Pieces of aggregate are placed in a container and crushed. The load required to produce 10 per cent fine particles (< 2.35 mm) is measured.

To provide sufficient strength and durability to resist crushing under compaction and traffic loads, granular materials in pervious pavements should have a 10 per cent fines value of greater than 100 kN when tested in accordance with British Standard BS 812: Part 111: 1990, *Testing aggregates methods* for determination of 10 per cent fines value.

Flakiness Index. This gives a measure of the flatness of the aggregate particles. It is the percentage of particles with a minimum thickness less than 60 per cent of the mean. A lower value represents more cuboid particles.

A maximum value of 25 per cent should ensure acceptable performance in granular materials below pervious pavements, when tested in accordance with British Standard BS 812: Section 105.1: 1989 *Flakiness index*.

Plate bearing tests on placed material. Plate bearing tests can be used on coarse aggregates that have been placed to determine the CBR value, in accordance with British Standard BS 1377: Part 9: 1990. The use of a 300 mm-diameter plate ensures that the presence of larger particles does not adversely affect the test results. The minimum CBR of open-graded aggregates should be 30 per cent.

Horizontal forces (for example, from braking or turning of heavy vehicles) need to be considered as they may cause granular layers to move over any impermeable geomembranes used to prevent infiltration. Again, the use of geogrids, geocellular confinement or roughened geomembranes should be considered in areas subject to a high level of braking or turning (Section 4.8).

The nature of the materials required to give suitable drainage characteristics may make them more susceptible to compression when subject to vibrations. This needs to be considered where heavy vehicles may stand with engines running (eg bus stops). It can be particularly problematic when block paving is bedded on uncompacted sand.

Using the grading curve, the permeability of the material may be crudely estimated using Hazen's formula (Hazen, 1911) or that proposed by Taylor (1948), see Box 4.6.

Box 4.6 *Estimating the permeability of granular materials*

Hazen's Formula – $k = C_1 (D_{10})^2$
Taylor's Formula – $k = (D_s)^2 (\gamma_w/\mu) (e^3/(1+e)) C$

Where:
k =   coefficient of permeability
D_{10} =   effective particle size in mm at which 10 per cent by weight of particles are smaller
D_s =   effective particle diameter, usually taken as D_{10}
C_1 =   constant taken as 0.01 to 0.015
C =   shape factor
γ_w =   unit weight of permeant (water)
μ =   viscosity of permeant (water)
e =   void ratio

Care should be adopted when using these equations; the results they provide should be confirmed by permeability testing.

4.5.2 Aggregate production

When specifying granular materials it is important to ensure that they can be easily, economically and sustainably produced. The use of the coarse crushed rock aggregates specified in BS 882: 1992 (see Table 4.4) will ensure that materials are readily available and can be produced economically.

Another consideration is the specification of the percentage content of particles below the 63 micron sieve size. The content below 5 mm is controlled by crushing, and the limits at 5 mm and 600 micron should be proportionate to the specified percentage passing the 63 micron sieve.

The Aggregate Tax, which came into force on 1 April 2002, initially applies a tax of £1.60 per tonne to sand, gravel and rock subjected to commercial exploitation in the UK. To minimise costs, recycled aggregate such as crushed concrete should be used wherever possible. Care should be taken when using recycled materials to ensure that leaching of contaminants does not occur (Section 4.5.1). Further guidance on the use of recycled materials is provided by Coventry *et al* (1999).

4.5.3 Strength improvement

The strength of granular layers can be improved by incorporating a geogrid or geocellular confinement system into the unbound layers (see Section 4.8). These give the material increased tensile resistance and stiffness to improve performance over weak subgrades and increase the design life of open-graded materials – see CIRIA Special Publication 123, Jewell, 1996).

Another method of improving the stiffness and strength of open-graded materials is to add small amounts of bituminous binder or Portland cement. The Portland Cement Association (1971) found that the addition of 330 kg/m^3 to 500 kg/m^3 of cement would be sufficient. It should be applied only to coat the aggregate, and care should be taken not to fill the voids with excess paste. Kazmierowski *et al* (1994) suggested the addition of 2–2.5 per cent bitumen significantly improves stability (and stiffness) of granular materials without significantly affecting permeability. Again, care should be taken to ensure the asphalt does not fill the voids.

4.6 CONTINUOUS SURFACES

4.6.1 Porous asphalt

The bituminous layers of a pervious pavement system need to be porous to allow the passage of water through. Porous asphalt, which has been used as a surface course in the UK, consists primarily of gap-graded aggregates held together by binder to form a matrix through which water can pass. Technical information available in the UK relates only to the use of porous asphalt surface courses that provide little structural capacity to a conventional pavement (Potter and Halliday, 1981).

The materials used conventionally in the binder course such as dense bitumen macadam (DBM) are stiff in comparison with the unbound layers, in order to minimise the thickness of construction. This has required materials with a high density and low air voids; in pervious systems, however, the opposite is required. There is no published guidance on the use of open-graded binder courses and bases, except in very lightly loaded applications such as private drives or small office car parks, where open-graded binder course may be used (Quarry Products Association, 2001).

In the United States, porous asphalt has been used to construct the structural layers in lightly loaded applications such as car parks. US practice (US Environmental Protection Agency, 1980) allows up to 100 mm of porous asphalt to be placed over the sub-base. The structural design of such a system could be carried out using equivalence factors (see Section 4.12) and allowance for reduced fatigue life due to embrittlement of the bitumen over time.

Specific guidance on the use of porous asphalt in surface courses is given in the DMRB, HD 37, Chapter 5. Asphalt with a nominal 20 mm aggregate size is favoured in the UK, as trials by TRL (Nicholls, 1997) showed this to have the best long-term performance. A specification for this material is provided in the *Specification for Highway Works* (Clause 938). British Standard BS 4987-1: 2001 gives specifications for several open-graded bituminous materials. These were used widely in the past as part of the construction for all types of classified road. Although not widely used now in conventional road pavement construction in the UK, they are suitable in pervious pavements in lightly loaded applications (for example, car parks). The materials that should be most appropriate to construct pervious asphalt surfaces are:

- 14 mm-size open-graded surface course
- 20 mm-size porous asphalt surface course
- 20 mm-size open-graded binder course.

These materials could be used for the full depth of bituminous construction in lightly loaded applications such as car parks, which would be similar to the practice adopted in the USA. British Standard BS 4987-1: 2001 includes materials with 10 mm aggregate, but these are more likely to clog and are not recommended for use in the applications discussed in this book.

The European Union's Construction Products Directive requires the use of performance specifications wherever practical. Therefore specifications based on performance requirements should allow a suitable material to be obtained. The clauses in the *Specification for Highway Works* relating to porous asphalt are now written in terms of performance, which is assessed by either laboratory testing, *in-situ* testing of laid material or by assessment and approval in advance under the British Board of Agrément scheme.

There is no reason why they cannot be developed providing account is taken of the reduced fatigue life of open-voided asphaltic materials. A very recent development is the use of porous asphalt that can carry heavy loads. The material comprises an open-textured mix of 28 mm to 40 mm aggregate with very few fines, together with a polymer modified binder. It has been successfully used on a trial section of the A4232 near Cardiff, and the Welsh Office is undertaking further trials on the M4 near Port Talbot (*New Civil Engineer*, 2002). It has been laid up to 150 mm thick and could be used in pervious surface construction.

Conventional bituminous materials may also be incorporated if suitable openings are left to allow water to pass through the material. This could be achieved by leaving openings in the material for water to percolate into the underlying granular layers. The size and position of the slots would need careful design to avoid compromising the integrity of the bituminous layers and prevention of clogging would have to be considered.

Durability

When designing pavements using porous asphalt or other open-graded bituminous mixes, allowance should be made for its reduced durability. Various trials have considered the durability of porous asphalt mixtures made with different binders. Modifiers and additives have been used to improve performance including synthetic rubber compounds, natural rubber, epoxy resins and fibres. The trials are reported in several TRL reports (Box 4.7), and guidance on binder content and modifiers is given in BS 4987-1: 2001.

Box 4.7   *TRL durability trials of porous asphalt*

1. Research Report RR57, *Pervious macadam, trials on trunk road A38 Burton Bypass* (M E Daines, 1984).
2. Research Report RR323, *Trials of pervious macadam and rolled asphalt on the A38 at Burton* (M E Daines, 1992).
3. Report 264, *Review of UK porous asphalt trials* (J C Nicholls, 1997).
4. Report 497, *The design of porous asphalt mixtures to performance related criteria* (J C Nicholls, 2001).
5. Report 499, *Material performance of porous asphalt including when laid over concrete* (J C Nicholls, 2001).

The key considerations regarding durability are:

*   the interconnected voids allow excellent access to air that potentially increases ageing and embrittlement. This requires binder modification (or recognition of the reduced design life)

- the expected life of porous asphalt is around seven to 10 years at traffic levels up to 6000 commercial vehicles per day per lane. This compares to a life of around 10 years for conventional hot-rolled asphalt wearing courses. Structural life under lower car park axle loading can be expected to be significantly greater because a softer binder can be used. In America, car parks constructed using porous asphalt have proved to still be structurally sound after 20 years.

Providing these factors are taken into account then there is no reason why porous asphalt systems cannot perform adequately. In car parks where HGV traffic is physically prevented, applied loads are much lower and consequently the expected structural life should be greater than 10 years.

4.6.2 *In-situ* concrete (rigid) pavements

There are three types of concrete pavement.

1. Jointed unreinforced.
2. Jointed reinforced.
3. Continuously reinforced.

Only jointed unreinforced may be used in pervious pavements constructed with porous concrete, as the requirement to allow water to percolate into the concrete pavement is incompatible with the presence of steel reinforcement in reinforced concrete. Where reinforcement is present the concrete must be dense and impermeable to protect the steel from corrosion and only permeable construction will be suitable (voids formed through the concrete surface).

The structural design of a pervious concrete pavement should be undertaken in the same way as a conventional one. Providing that the strength of the concrete is specified and achieved then they should perform adequately. There is a lot of experience in using porous concrete in pipes, where adequate strengths are achieved.

It is important to note that joints should be sealed and not used as water infiltration pathways. This is because the joints are required to allow expansion and contraction of the pavement without uncontrolled cracking occurring. If debris gets into the cracks then expansion can be prevented, leading to failure of the pavement.

In-situ concrete pervious pavements, constructed with porous concrete, have been used in the USA. Concrete pavements with voids through the construction to allow water to pass through (permeable construction) have been used in the UK.

4.7 ELEMENTAL SURFACES

4.7.1 Reinforced gravel/grass systems

Reinforced gravel and grass systems are generally designed in accordance with manufacturer's design guidance documents or prescribed layer thickness. They are typically only suitable for lightly trafficked areas, or where very occasional heavy traffic occurs. The use of geogrids and/or geocellular confinement systems below other surfaces, within the sub-base layer, provides the potential for use in heavily trafficked applications.

There are two types.

1. Rigid geosynthetic or concrete structures that act as, and should be designed as, blocks.
2. Flexible geoysnthetics that act to confine lateral movement and thus increase stiffness (cellular confinement) (Box 4.8).

Cellular confinement systems produce a stiff base with high flexural strength. Acting like a semi-rigid slab, loads are distributed laterally reducing subgrade contact pressures and increasing the bearing capacity of the underlying soils. The systems can provide a stable base for paved surfaces and surface stabilisation for unpaved surfaces.

Box 4.8   *Cellular confinement*

Unsurfaced pavements consist of layers of aggregate placed and compacted on soil subgrades. The fill materials allow the system to support traffic loads that, by itself, the soil would not be able to withstand. The function of the base material is to distribute the imposed loads over a larger area, reducing the pressure transferred to the subgrade. The base material is able to distribute the loads because the individual aggregate particles lock together. Applied loads are transmitted through the base material both as vertical and horizontal forces. If the horizontal (lateral) forces push the base material sideways, rutting develops. The result is a thinner layer less able to resist additional load applications, which leads to failure.

To prevent lateral movement within the aggregate, cellular confinement can be introduced. The plastic grids hold the aggregate together and the tensile strength of the plastic resists the lateral forces and prevents rutting. It also significantly reduces the pressure applied to the subgrade by a load exerted on the top surface of the confinement layer (Figure 4.4)

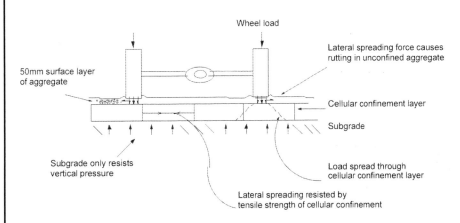

Figure 4.4   *Cellular confinement*

The design of cellular confinement layers can be undertaken using methods developed by the US Army Engineer Waterways Experiment Station (Mitchell *et al*, 1979). In addition, many books detail methods for reinforcing soils with geosynthetic materials. Some manufacturers provide equivalent layer thickness comparisons between their product and conventional aggregate construction. The pavement can then be designed as unreinforced and the required cellular confinement layer substituted into the design.

4.7.2   Concrete blocks

Although some manufacturers' design guides are available. block paving structures for conventional applications should be designed in accordance with BS 7533 (BSI, 2001). There are two parts to the British Standard.

1. BS 7533: Part 1: 2001 *Pavements constructed with clay, natural aggregate or concrete pavers. Part 1: Guide for the structural design of heavy duty pavements constructed of clay pavers or precast concrete paving blocks*. This is for pavements carrying between 0.5 msa and 12 msa.

2. BS 7533: Part 2: 2001 *Pavements constructed with clay, natural aggregate or concrete pavers. Part 2: Guide for the structural design of lightly trafficked pavements constructed of clay pavers or precast concrete paving blocks.* This is for pavements carrying less than 0.5 msa.

For structural design purposes, BS 7533 considers concrete block pavements to behave as flexible pavements. They are generally well suited structurally to use in pervious pavement systems and there are no specific structural design requirements in relation to this use over and above those discussed for the other materials used below the blocks.

For lightly trafficked areas, BS 7533: Part 2: 2001 can be used to design pervious pavements and only requires a sub-base and laying course below block paving. Lightly trafficked areas are defined in Table 4.5.

Table 4.5   *BS 7533: Part 2: 2001* Requirements for lightly trafficked block paving areas

Category	Typical applications
II	> 5 commercial vehicles/day (cv/d)
	Adopted highways and other roads less than 0.5 msa for example, culs-de-sac, pedestrianised areas subject to regular trafficking by heavy axle loads
	≤ 5 cv/d
	Car parks receiving occasional heavy traffic
	Footways regularly overidden by vehicular traffic
IIIa	Pedestrianised areas receiving occasional heavy traffic
	Footways overridden by occasional vehicular traffic
IIIb	Car parks receiving no heavy traffic
	Footways likely to be overridden by no more than occasional vehicular traffic
IV	Private drives, hard landscaping or areas that receive no vehicular traffic (eg school playgrounds)

Providing the sub-base meets the performance criteria defined in Section 4.5, and the CBR of the subgrade takes into account the presence of water, then no other special considerations are required in these areas for the structural design of pervious block pavement systems.

BS 7533: Part 1: 2001 does require the use of dense bitumen macadam (DBM) or cement-bound material (CBM) as a base. As discussed in Section 4.6.1, these materials are not pervious. They will need to be replaced with other materials, based on equivalence and backed up by testing. It should be possible to produce a specification for a cement-bound material that has sufficient void space and hence permeability for use in pervious pavement systems, using single-size aggregates. Alternatively, conventional bituminous materials may be incorporated if suitable openings are left to allow water to pass through to the underlying granular layers. Careful detailing will be required to ensure the openings do not compromise the integrity of the placed materials.

4.7.3   Synthetic geocellular structures

Where synthetic geocellular structures are used below trafficked areas, several issues arise:

- stiffness, shear and bending resistance – the structures need to be designed to carry the required loads
- long-term creep behaviour under load – plastics tend to deform under constant load

- performance under horizontal loads – from braking
- resistance to chemicals – diesel and petrol in particular – from spillage (spillage also affects bitumen-bound materials such as asphalt).

Design of these type of structures requires the use of basic structural and soil mechanics theory, rather than pavement design methods, as they behave as a rigid foundation and should not suffer large permanent deformations under repeated low-level loading (See Figure 4.5).

The strength and stiffness characteristics of geosynthetic structures differ from conventional aggregates. Conventional aggregates typically have significantly lower ultimate strengths and higher stiffness than geosynthetics. Aggregates also suffer permanent deformations under much lower loads and do not have any tensile strength. Geosynthetics suffer from long-term creep under constant load and possibly fatigue under repeated short-term loads, and this should be addressed in design of the structure.

These characteristics mean that the use of conventional pavement design methods are not applicable, as they are based on serviceability criterion. For geosynthetic structures, both ultimate and serviceability limit state structural analysis should be undertaken.

The structural analysis should take account of the compressive, tensile and shear properties of the structure, which will increase load spread and thus reduce the applied stress on the underlying subgrade and thus vertical movements. The vertical stress distribution in the subgrade may be estimated using the Boussinesq equation or commonly assumed load spread distributions and the applied wheel loads, contact area and tyre pressures. This is shown in the figure below.

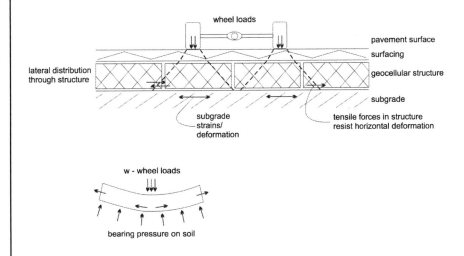

In a similar manner to conventional structural design, partial load and material factors should be applied to allow for variation in the loads and material properties. The material partial factors should take account of factors such as creep test results, the length of time creep testing was undertaken, quality control testing during manufacture, and the risk of physical or environmental damage to the structures. Guidance on the choice of partial material factors for synthetic earth reinforcement is given by Ingold (1994) and this can be applied to geo-cellular structures.

The applied loading should be similar to other structures and therefore partial load factors used in other fields of structural design can be used. Appropriate values for load partial factors are provided in BS 8110 (1997).

Because the analysis is a static design and wheel loads are dynamic, factors should be applied to allow for this, and any design using this procedure should be adequately validated by *in-situ* testing on trial sections of pavement.

Figure 4.5 *Design of synthetic geocellular structures*

Synthetic geocellular systems should have independent laboratory test results for the following parameters to allow design using conventional structural methods and to demonstrate satisfactory performance:

- bending resistance
- compressive and tensile strength and stiffness
- long-term creep characteristics.

There is a popular misconception that plastic materials are unsuitable for use below car parks and hardstanding areas because they will be attacked by diesel and petrol spillage. Although the common materials used in these structures (polypropylene or high-density polyethylene) can be attacked by some of the chemicals at high concentrations or at elevated temperatures, in practice it is unlikely to occur in everyday situations because they will be diluted to low concentrations. In addition, the contact time will be low, which reduces the risk of damage occurring. The risk from spillages should be assessed on the basis of the likelihood of such an event occurring and the probable consequences. Further information is provided in BS CP 312: Part 1: 1973 or in manufacturers' product-specific literature.

4.8 GEOTEXTILES AND GEOGRIDS

To reduce the effects of water on the strength and stiffness properties of the subgrade below pervious pavements, a geotextile separator layer should always be provided over moisture-sensitive or fine-grained subgrades (Figure 4.6). This will enhance the performance of the pavement structure in two ways.

1. It will prevent pumping of finer soils into the open-graded aggregate of the unbound layers.
2. It will provide enhanced resistance to deformation of the subgrade under load, by providing a tensile resistance.

Geogrids or geocellular confinement systems may also be incorporated into the granular layers to increase the stiffness and therefore reduce the required thickness of the layers. They can also be used as separation layers to prevent migration of fine particles between unbound layers (see Section 4.1) and play an important role in removing pollutants (see Chapter 5 and Appendix A6).

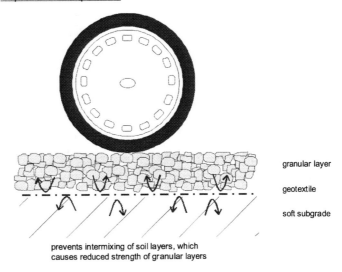

Separation Component

granular layer

geotextile

soft subgrade

prevents intermixing of soil layers, which
causes reduced strength of granular layers

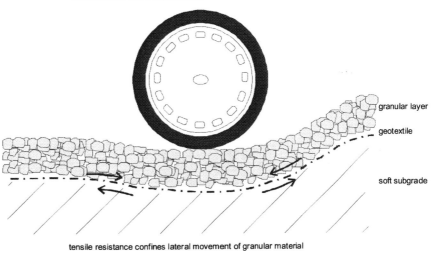

Confinement Component

granular layer

geotextile

soft subgrade

tensile resistance confines lateral movement of granular material

Figure 4.6 *Geotextiles resisting the forces applied to the pavement*

The choice of geotextile should be based on the required performance characteristics,
including strength, puncture resistance and the criteria for filtration (Section 6.4).

4.9 GEOMEMBRANES

If an impermeable geomembrane is required to prevent water infiltration, create
attenuation or prevent softening of the subgrade, it should be able to withstand the loads
imposed during construction and the service life of the pavement. It should be
manufactured from a robust material such as polypropylene or high-density
polyethylene (HDPE). The advantages and disadvantages of these materials are discussed
in CIRIA Special Publication 124 (Privett *et al*, 1996), together with the properties
required and suggested testing methods (see Box 4.9). To ensure it is impermeable it
should have homogeneous welded joints and be installed under a CQA system to
ensure no water can penetrate into the subgrade. In addition, it is good practice to protect
the geomembrane from damage on both faces with a geotextile fleece or sand layer.

Box 4.9   *Geomembrane properties*

Testing of geomembranes is either:

- material property testing
- material seam testing.

Material property testing

Material property testing is carried out on samples in the laboratory. No British Standards exist, although it is planned to publish them when the European (CEN) Standards are issued. At present, the most accepted methods of testing are either American or German. The properties most commonly specified are set out in the table below.

Property	USA Standard test method	German Standard test method
Physical		
Thickness	ASTM D751 or D1593	DIN 53370
Density	ASTM D792 or D1505	DIN 53479
Melt flow index	ASTM D1238 E	DIN ISO 1133
Carbon black percentage	ASTM D1603	*
Mechanical		
Tensile behaviour	ASTM D638	DIN 53455
Tear resistance	ASTM D1004	DIN 53515
Impact resistance	ASTM D1822	DIN 53488
Puncture resistance	"FTMS 101C, method 2065+"	DIN 54307
Dimensional stability	ASTM D1204	DIN 53377
Stress crack resistance	ASTM D1693	*
Chemical		
Swelling resistance	ASTM D570	DIN 53495
Ozone resistance	ASTM D518	*
Ultraviolet resistance	ASTM D3334	DIN 53387

* No standard test method
+ US General Services Administration, Method 2065, Federal test method Standard 101C.

Detailed information on the specification of geomembrane properties is given in CIRIA Special Publication 124 (Privett *et al*, 1996).

Material seam testing

Seam testing is carried out to assess the quality of the geomembrane seaming operation on site. Destructive seam tests require samples to be cut out and tested in a laboratory for either shear strength or peeling resistance. Non-destructive testing is carried out in place on the sealed membrane. CIRIA SP124 (Privett *et al*, 1996) provides a detailed discussion on the merits of different test methods.

Because the test methods are different, care should be taken in the choice of acceptance criteria, which should be relevant to the test method used. Properties should always be specified on the basis of the required performance of the membrane in any given situation.

The performance of pavement systems requires full friction to develop between the layers of materials. Care is required when incorporating geomembranes to ensure that the strength of the overlying construction will still be able to carry the required loads.

Where geomembranes are provided, the overlying layers should also have sufficient thickness and friction properties to ensure that the pavement can adequately resist horizontal forces (eg braking) at the geomembrane/aggregate interface. If necessary, geogrid reinforcement may be incorporated into the sub-base at areas where excessive horizontal forces are expected to be encountered (Figure 4.7).

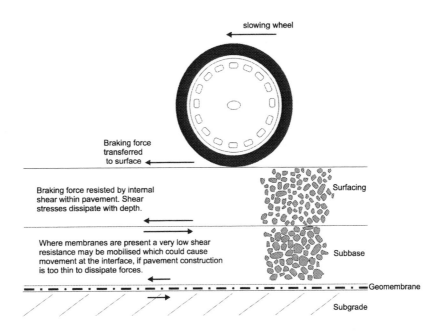

Figure 4.7 *Impact of braking forces on geomembrane*

4.10   WETTING AND DRYING

The effects of prolonged exposure to wetting/drying cycles will also need to be considered, particularly for plastic clays near trees. In these situations, the clay dries and shrinks when trees remove moisture and swells again when moisture is added. The resulting cracks in the clay then allow infiltrating water to penetrate deeper into the clay and cause a greater zone of softening.

These effects will be most severe where clay subgrades are highly shrinkable and have a plasticity index greater than 40 per cent as defined in the *National House Building Council Standards*, Chapter 4.2 (NHBC, 1999). In such cases, a geomembrane system should be provided to prevent water contact with the subgrade. For all other subgrades, the CBR values should be measured after subjecting samples to a series of wetting and drying cycles.

To reduce the effects of trees, either greater-than-normal falls in subgrade levels and pipes should be allowed or trees should be planted where they will not influence the soils below the pavement. Further guidance on these effects is provided in the *National House Building Council Standards* (NHBC, 1999), Volume 4, Chapter 4.2, "Building Near Trees".

4.11   INFILTRATION

To allow infiltration of the surface water into the underlying subgrade, the soils should be of sufficient permeability and a suitable depth above the water table. Such systems are suitable only for permeable rocks, sand and gravel. Generally, the stiffness of such materials is not significantly affected by increases in moisture content, and the use of infiltration systems should not adversely affect structural performance. The exception to this is where there is a high content of fine particles, such as in fine silty or clayey sands. In these materials, where the percentage passing the 63 micron sieve is greater than 30 per cent, the stiffness can be reduced significantly and the structural performance of the pavement may be affected. In these situations, a geotextile separator, geogrids or geocellular confinement may be used to increase stiffness of the granular layers, if an infiltration system is required (Section 4.8).

Infiltration systems should be designed in accordance with CIRIA Report 156 (Bettess, 1996).

4.12 DESIGNS BASED ON EQUIVALENCE FACTORS

The use of equivalence factors is a method to allow experience gained from previous full-scale trials on proven materials to be applied to paving materials of which there is little or no previous experience. Equivalence factors were used when concrete block paving was first introduced in the UK and could be a useful design approach to assist in the acceptance of pervious pavements. It is based on work by Knapton (1976). The approach is also the basis for the British Ports Federation design manual (Knapton and Meletiou, 1996). The tests comprised measuring the load-spreading capability of blocks, sub-base and asphalt and comparing the results to give an equivalent thickness of block construction to replace asphalt.

The British Ports Federation method uses a combination of equivalence and analytical methods. The thickness of any layer in the pavement is converted to an equivalent thickness of one that would limit vertical strain to the same amount. Based on this work, Knapton (1989) produced a table of equivalence factors for different paving materials. BS 7533: Part 1: 2001, Table 4 also provides equivalence values (referred to as material conversion factors) for evaluating highway pavement materials, comparing their performance to 100 pen dense bitumen macadam. Equivalence factors for a range of materials are provided in Table 4.6.

It should be possible to use the equivalence or material conversion factors from Knapton and BS 7533 to replace DBM with porous asphalt and sub-base in designs. This will require testing to determine the elastic modulus and Poisson's ratio of the materials used. The relative thickness of layers formed from different materials can be calculated using the following equation:

$$H_2 = H_1 \ x \ \sqrt{(E_1/E_2)x\left[\left(1-\upsilon_2^2\right)/\left(1-\upsilon_1^2\right)\right]}$$

where:

H_1 and H_2 = thickness of layer

E_1 and E_2 = elastic modulus

υ_1 and υ_2 = Poisson's ratio.

Table 4.6 *Material conversion factors from BS 7533-1 and Knapton (1989)*

Category of material	Suggested material conversion factor (mcf)
Dense bitumen macadam 100 pen	1
Hot-rolled asphalt	1
80 mm blocks on 30 mm laying course	1
Open-textured macadam	0.7
Type 1 sub-base over material with CBR > 5%	0.3
Type 1 sub-base over material with CBR < 5%	0.2
CBM 1	0.4
CBM 2	0.5
CBM 3 or 4	0.7
Subgrade improvement material (capping layer)	0.1

The reliability of the equivalence factors depends on the accuracy of laboratory testing to determine equivalence and may overlook the long-term benefit or disbenefit, durability and fatigue resistance of a material. Care is also required when the two materials being compared differ greatly in their engineering properties.

4.13 WINTER BEHAVIOUR

4.13.1 Freeze-thaw of saturated layers

The US Environmental Protection Agency (USEPA, 1972) tested porous asphalt samples over 265 freeze-thaw cycles and no physical dimensional changes were observed. TRL Report 264 also looked at the potential problem of saturated layers becoming frozen, and the expansion of water as it turns to ice damaging the structure. No cases of rapid failure that would result from such damage were observed and there are no reports of such damage in international literature. Although there are no reports on the performance of concrete or block systems, the same is likely to be true.

The pavements at Walden Ponds in the USA were reported to show no ill effects after repeated freeze-thaw cycles, and laboratory tests on the materials confirmed this (Wei, 1986). This is because the voids have sufficient volume to accommodate expansion. The underlying granular sub-base and capping have even greater void space and should not be affected. However, ice mushrooms have been observed when freezing water expanded through the voids in the upper surface.

The Road Research Laboratory (1952) provided guidance on soils affected by frost. Silty sands are most affected by frost heave, so, providing the requirements for aggregate gradings given in Section 4.5 are followed (D_2 greater than 2.54 mm), then frost heave should not be a problem. This should be confirmed by undertaking tests in accordance with British Standard BS 812: Part 124: 1989.

The sub-base material should not become fully saturated. To prevent this, and to leave space for water volume expansion on freezing, the design storage volume should be increased by 30 per cent.

4.13.2 Frost resistance

There is no evidence that any of the pervious pavement systems adversely affect the depth of frost penetration into the ground. Indeed, the open-voided nature of the materials, with a high air content, may be beneficial and reduce the depth of frost penetration (Figure 4.8). The standard requirement in the UK for the materials within 450 mm of the ground surface to be frost-resistant is also applicable to pervious pavements, therefore, unless it is proved they can limit frost penetration to a shallower depth, for example by providing a continuous insulating layer of air when they are at maximum designed water storage capacity.

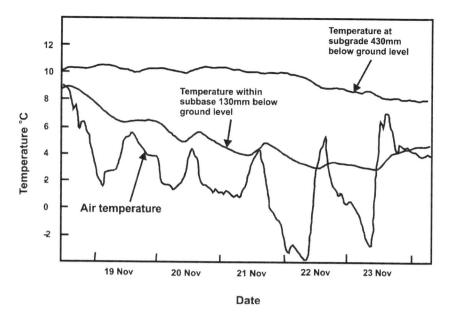

Figure 4.8 *Temperature variation below a pervious pavement at Clifton car park (CIRIA, 1995)*

The effect of lower conductivity of open-graded materials affects the way the ice forms on the surface of pervious pavements. TRL Report 264 (Nicholls, 1997) discusses the effects on porous asphalt surfaces. Colder conditions result from the lower thermal conductivity and higher humidity in the voids relative to the air and the following occur more frequently:

* hoar frosts on the surface
* ice formation (but in thinner layers)
* snow settles earlier and stays longer.

This has implications for winter maintenance:

* use of salt rather than grit for de icing
* more frequent applications of de-icing materials but at a lower rate of deposition each time.

4.14   REFLECTIVE CRACKING

Where synthetic geocellular structures are overlain by bituminous materials, reflective cracking can occur in the surfacing (ie cracks from the joints propagate upwards through the bituminous layers).

This can be overcome by incorporating geogrids into the bituminous materials. A similar problem occurs when concrete roads are overlain by bituminous materials and there is a great deal of experience in incorporating the grids into asphalt or macadam (Ingold, 1994).

5 Water quality performance issues

5.1 POLLUTION AND PERVIOUS SURFACES

Surface water runoff can wash pollutants into watercourses or the soil. The nature and the amount of pollution is dependent upon the land use and human activities within a catchment. Similarly, the impact of surface water runoff is difficult to predict as it is dependent not only upon the type and mass of pollution transported, the concentration of pollutant and volume of runoff, but also upon the nature and sensitivity of the receiving waters and runoff rates and volumes. In addition, the effects may be cumulative and the impacts may change with time as a catchment becomes urbanised or as levels of activity change.

In rural or urban areas, pervious surfaces, together with their associated substructures, may be used to intercept surface water runoff and so limit the direct discharge of pollutants to receiving waters. The source of pollutants may derive from activities on the pervious surface, such as car parking leading to oil deposits, or may come from adjacent areas and activities on them, such as the deposit of airborne fertiliser spray. In addition, the pollution input may be at a low level and over a long period due to general and appropriate activities, but it may also be rapid and uncontrolled, such as in the event of a spillage. The design and long-term performance of pervious surfaces needs to take into account this potential variability of environmental conditions over the operating life.

The pollutants of most concern in highway or car park runoff are:

- sediments
- metals (zinc, copper, cadmium)
- hydrocarbons (oil and fuel) including polycyclic aromatic hydrocarbons (PAH)
- pesticides and herbicides (from landscaping maintenance)
- chlorides (from de-icing).

An indication of levels of some pollutants in runoff from urban areas is given in Table 5.1. Luker and Montague (1994) also give guidance on the pollutant runoff from highways.

Potentially polluting substances exist widely, but in their dispersed state and with the naturally occurring physical, chemical and biological processes in the environment they may be harmless to flora and fauna. For example, most urban surfaces contain metals that when present in small quantities spread over a wide area are harmless to plants. Stormwater drainage is one mechanism that may concentrate these diffuse pollutants by washing them off a surface, increasing the concentration and/or the load of pollutants, to potentially harmful effect.

Pervious surfaces limit the concentration of pollutants in surface water runoff by immediate, localised interception. Because water does not flow across the surface, pollutants on the surface either remain there or are taken into the surface immediately below by the local percolating water.

Table 5.1 *Event mean concentrations and unit loads for pollutants in urban stormwater runoff (Hall et al, 1993)*

	Observed event mean concentrations (average) (mg/l or g/m³)	Load per unit area (average) (kg/imp ha/yr)
Suspended solids (SS)	21 to 2582 (187)	347 to 2340 (487)
Total volatile solids (TVS)	26 to 149 (73)	90 to 127 (98)
BOD_5	7 to 22 (11)	35 to 172 (59)
COD	20 to 365 (85)	22 to 703 (358)
Ammoniacal nitrogen	0.2 to 4.6 (1.45)	1.2 to 25.1 (1.76)
Total inorganic nitrogen	0.5 to 8.8 (2.1)	n/a
Total phosphorous (P_{tot})	0.04 to 0.76 (0.34)	0.5 to 4.9 (1.8)
Total lead (Pb_{tot})	0.03 to 3.1 (0.21)	0.09 to 1.91 (0.83)
Total zinc (Zn_{tot})	0.05 to 3.68 (0.3)	0.21 to 2.68 (1.15)
Total copper (Cu_{tot})	0.02 to 0.35 (0.11)	0.06 to 1.05 (0.46)
Oil	0.09 to 2.8 (0.4)	n/a
Faecal coliforms (E.coli)	400 to 50 000 (6430) (MPN/100ml)	0.9 to 3.8 (2.1) (× 109 counts/ha)

5.2   IMPACTS OF POLLUTION

Having intercepted surface water and pollutants, pervious surfaces may facilitate the movement of those pollutants, particularly the dissolved ones, either into the soil below the construction, and hence possibly into groundwater, or into the receiving surface waters. The impacts of pollution are many and varied and have been extensively covered in both the scientific and general media. They range from the rapid and life-threatening to the slow long-term degradation of an environment. An example of the former might be a bulk leakage from a milk tanker into a watercourse, which could result in the depletion of oxygen in the water, as the milk is degraded by biological and chemical processes that consume oxygen, leading to widespread fish kill. Alternatively, the slow accumulation of silt and sediment transported in surface water runoff and deposited on feeding or spawning grounds in a stream may affect the viability of some aquatic species, which in turn could influence the whole food chain in the stream.

The impact may be caused by a pollutant in the dissolved or solid phase and this may change according to the environmental conditions – some heavy metals are sensitive to changes in the acidity of the runoff, for example. Heavy metals such as cadmium, zinc, copper and lead may be transported in association with sediments in their solid form or may be dissolved and transported rapidly with the flow. Cadmium and zinc are often present largely in the dissolved form, whereas copper and lead tend to be sediment-associated. Nutrients such as nitrates, phosphates and potassium encourage plant and algal growth, which may harm or adversely affect flora and fauna. Being transported in the aqueous-phase nutrients, pesticides and herbicides are easily moved through the environment within surface and ground waters. Hydrocarbons (oil, petrol, diesel and PAH) can be transported into the groundwater or surface waters, either miscible in water or as free-phase liquids.

It is important to consider the source of a pollutant and its persistence in the environment. Point sources are generally easily identifiable, such as discharges from poorly performing sewage treatment works. Diffuse sources are more widespread, such as storm drainage discharges to a watercourse, and may be more difficult to control. Contaminants such as heavy metals are very persistent in the environment. They do not break down and remain for very long periods of time. Others, such as hydrocarbons, may degrade and do not remain in the environment for long. These factors need to be considered carefully when assessing the risks a pervious pavement poses to controlled waters.

A fully documented qualitative risk assessment of the impacts of a pervious surface on the receiving waters should always be undertaken and the results fully communicated to the developers/owners (Box 5.1). This should take account of the sensitivity of the receiving environment.

Box 5.1

Box 5.1 *Risk assessment for pervious surfaces*

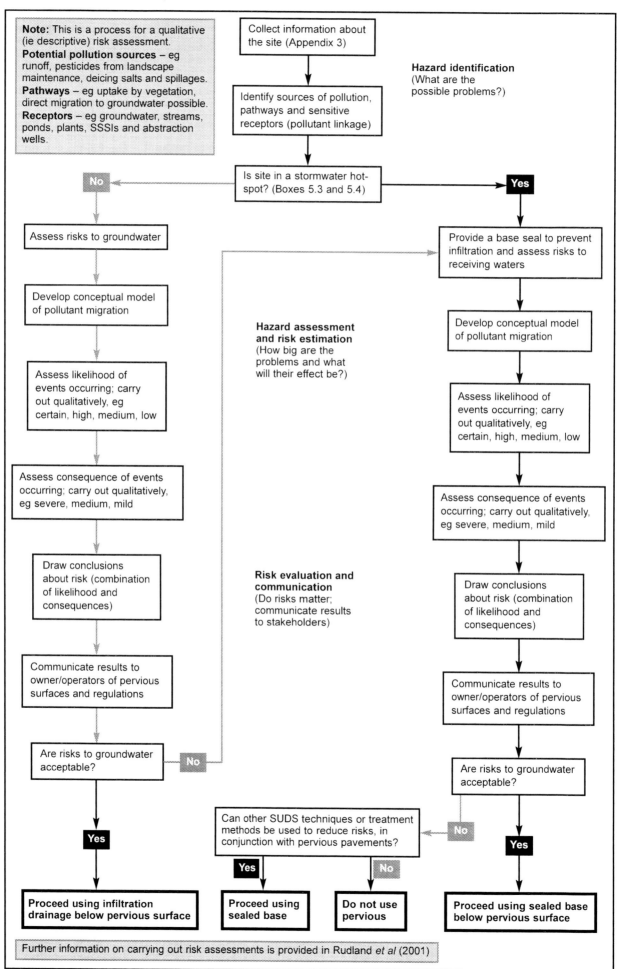

Note: This is a process for a qualitative (ie descriptive) risk assessment.
Potential pollution sources – eg runoff, pesticides from landscape maintenance, deicing salts and spillages.
Pathways – eg uptake by vegetation, direct migration to groundwater possible.
Receptors – eg groundwater, streams, ponds, plants, SSSIs and abstraction wells.

Collect information about the site (Appendix 3)

Hazard identification
(What are the possible problems?)

Identify sources of pollution, pathways and sensitive receptors (pollutant linkage)

Is site in a stormwater hot-spot? (Boxes 5.3 and 5.4)

No / Yes

Assess risks to groundwater

Provide a base seal to prevent infiltration and assess risks to receiving waters

Develop conceptual model of pollutant migration

Hazard assessment and risk estimation
(How big are the problems and what will their effect be?)

Develop conceptual model of pollutant migration

Assess likelihood of events occurring; carry out qualitatively, eg certain, high, medium, low

Assess likelihood of events occurring; carry out qualitatively, eg certain, high, medium, low

Assess consequence of events occurring; carry out qualitatively, eg severe, medium, mild

Assess consequence of events occurring; carry out qualitatively, eg severe, medium, mild

Draw conclusions about risk (combination of likelihood and consequences)

Risk evaluation and communication
(Do risks matter; communicate results to stakeholders)

Draw conclusions about risk (combination of likelihood and consequences)

Communicate results to owner/operators of pervious surfaces and regulations

Communicate results to owner/operators of pervious surfaces and regulations

Are risks to groundwater acceptable?

No

Are risks to groundwater acceptable?

Yes

Can other SUDS techniques or treatment methods be used to reduce risks, in conjunction with pervious pavements?

No

Yes

Yes / No

Proceed using infiltration drainage below pervious surface

Proceed using sealed base

Do not use pervious

Proceed using sealed base below pervious surface

Further information on carrying out risk assessments is provided in Rudland *et al* (2001)

5.3 LEGISLATION

The Water Resources Act (1991) and the Groundwater Regulations (1998) are the main items of legislation protecting controlled waters in England and Wales, although other legislation also includes provision in this respect (Box 5.2). They protect aquifers by forbidding the discharge of pollutants to groundwater, particularly substances in Lists I and II. In addition, environmental regulators have policies for protecting groundwater quality (Environment Agency, 1998). In England and Wales, the Environment Agency has defined groundwater source protection zones around public water supply boreholes, to ensure the installation and operation of appropriate pollution control measures to prevent contamination. In association with the EA policy, criteria on the use of infiltration techniques with various land uses have been developed (Box 5.3).

In Scotland, the policy relating to the use of sustainable drainage techniques, including infiltration techniques, is provided in Scottish Environment Protection Agency Policy No 1 (SEPA, 1996) and Policy No 15 (SEPA, 2001). These criteria not only define when infiltration may be used but also indicate when pre-treatment of waters may be required, the detail of which will be discussed at the planning stage of a development. Although pervious surface systems do have some pre-treatment capability, it is not formally recognised and a cautious approach should be adopted in this respect to ensure the system operates as required.

In Northern Ireland policy is defined in *Policy and practice for the protection of groundwater in Northern Ireland* (Department of the Environment in Northern Ireland, 2001).

Box 5.2 *Summary of environmental legislation applicable to pervious surfaces*

England and Wales

The Water Resources Act 1991 and the Groundwater Regulations 1998 provide the main body of control relating to the prevention and control of water pollution in England and Wales. In addition, other statutes contain provisions that relate to control and prevention of pollution or the maintenance of water quality standards. These include:

- The Salmon and Freshwater Fisheries Act 1975
- Environmental Protection Act 1990
- The Land Drainage Act 1991
- The Environment Act 1995.

Controlled waters are defined in the WRA 1991 as:

- inland fresh waters – rivers, streams, lakes, ponds and canals
- groundwater – water contained in underground soils and rocks
- coastal waters – all estuarine waters up to the freshwater limits of rivers and streams.

The Groundwater Regulations require that List I substances must be prevented from entering groundwater and List II substances must be controlled to prevent pollution of groundwater.

It is a criminal offence for a person or company to pollute, or knowingly permit the pollution, of controlled waters.

List I includes relevant substances such as cadmium, mineral oils and hydrocarbons. **List II** includes relevant substances such as heavy metals and MTBE.

For a pervious pavement, these substances will be at lower concentrations at the outlet than a conventional system and hydrocarbons will degrade inside the pavement structure, unlike in conventional drains. Note also that oil interceptors used on conventional drains do not stop dissolved contaminants or those adsorbed to very fine sediments entering controlled waters.

---

continued on next page...

These are important considerations for all pervious pavements and also conventional drainage, especially if soakaways are used, and the designer should assess the risks posed to controlled waters by the water that passes through the system. This applies to both infiltration and tanked systems that outflow through pipes into watercourses.

Scotland

The main legislation relating to the prevention and control of water pollution in Scotland is:

● The Control of Pollution Act 1974 as amended by the Environment Act 1995
● The Groundwater Regulations 1998.

Controlled waters in Scotland are defined in the Control of Pollution Act and the definition is similar to that for England and Wales. The Groundwater Regulations also apply in Scotland so that List I substances must be prevented from entering groundwater and List II substances must be controlled to prevent pollution of groundwater.

Details of Scottish policy on infiltration drainage and SUDS are provided in the Scottish Environment Protection Agency Policy Numbers 1 and 15 (SEPA, 1996 and 2001). SEPA policy is to promote SUDS schemes, including pervious surfaces, and encourage their design to be undertaken in accordance with the CIRIA design manual for Scotland and Northern Ireland (CIRIA, 2001a).

Northern Ireland

Regulation of water quality issues in Northern Ireland is the responsibility of the Environment and Heritage Service, which is an agency of the Department of the Environment in Northern Ireland. The main legislation relating to protection of controlled waters in Northern Ireland is:

● Water Act (Northern Ireland) 1972
● Groundwater Regulations (Northern Ireland) 1998
● Water (Northern Ireland) Order 1999 (when fully implemented this will replace the Water Act (Northern Ireland) 1972).

The Environment and Heritage Service promotes and regulates the conservation of water resources and the cleanliness of water in waterways and underground strata in accordance with the Water Act (Northern Ireland) 1972.

"Underground strata" is defined as "strata subjacent to the surface of any land, and any reference to water contained in any underground strata is a reference to water so contained" (but excluding public sewers, pipes, reservoirs and tanks).

Waterways include any river, stream, watercourse, inland water (whether natural or artificial) or tidal waters and any channel or passage of whatever kind (whether natural or artificial) through which water flows (but excluding public sewers and drains).

The Environment and Heritage Service policy in relation to infiltration drainage is described in the *Policy and practice for the protection of groundwater in Northern Ireland* (Department of the Environment Northern Ireland, 2001). This is similar to Environment Agency policy. It includes information on source protection zones and groundwater vulnerability, and states "Disposal of surface drainage water to underground strata should have due regard to the contamination risk posed to groundwater".

The Groundwater Regulations (Northern Ireland) 1998 require that List I substances must be prevented from entering groundwater and List II substances must be controlled to prevent pollution of groundwater.

The Environment Agency policy in relation to infiltration drainage is based on the Groundwater Protection Policy (Environment Agency, 1998). This is based on the concept of groundwater vulnerability, which is defined simply as a measure of the ease with which unacceptable effects on groundwater resources can occur. It describes aquifer protection in terms of both source and resource protection. The vulnerability depends on site-specific factors such as geology, depth of unsaturated zone and location of abstraction wells. The table below shows the Environment Agency's acceptability matrix for discharges to the ground (from *Groundwater Protection Policy*, Environment Agency, 1998).

	Source protection		
Activity	**I Inner zone**	**II Outer zone**	**III Catchment zone**
Roof drainage	No objection (R5) providing for sole use of roof drainage	No objection (R5)	No objection (R5)
Impermeable areas			
- public/ amenity	Not acceptable (R1)	Acceptable (R4)	Acceptable (R4)
- large car parks	Not acceptable (R1)	Acceptable (R3/4) with interceptor	Acceptable (R4) with interceptor
- lorry parks	Not acceptable (R1)	Presumption against (R2)	Acceptable (R3/4) with interceptor
- garage forecourts	Not acceptable (R1)	Presumption against (R2)	Acceptable (R4) with interceptor
- major roads	Not acceptable (R1)	Presumption against (R2) Acceptable only in exceptional circumstances	Acceptable only if investigation favourable and with adequate precautions (R4)
Industrial sites	Not acceptable (R1)	Presumption against (R2)	Acceptable only if investigation favourable and with adequate precautions (R3/4)
	Resource protection		
Activity	**Major aquifer**	**Minor aquifer**	**Non-aquifer**
Roof drainage	No objection (R5)	No objection (R5)	No objection (R5)
Impermeable areas			
- public/ amenity	Acceptable (R4)	Acceptable (R4)	Acceptable (R4)
- large car parks	Acceptable (R4) with interceptor	Acceptable (R4) with interceptor	Acceptable (R4) with interceptor
- lorry parks	Acceptable (R4) with interceptor	Acceptable (R4) with interceptor	Acceptable (R4) with interceptor
- garage fore- courts	Acceptable (R4) with interceptor	Acceptable (R4) with interceptor	Acceptable (R4) with interceptor
- major roads	Acceptable (R4) subject to investigation and with interceptor	Acceptable (R4) subject to investigation and with interceptor	Acceptable (R4) with interceptor
Industrial sites	Acceptable only if investigation favourable and with adequate precautions (R3/4)	Acceptable (R4) subject to investigation and with interceptor	Acceptable (R4) subject to investigation and with interceptor

R1 Prohibit/object in principle
R2 Presumption against
R3 Prohibition notice/consent to discharge

R4 No objection subject to standard conditions
R5 No objection

Note that discharge consent will not be permitted for List I substances.
Groundwater pollution cannot be seen and is difficult to put right once it has occurred. Therefore, the precautionary principle should be adopted when assessing risks to groundwater and deciding if to use infiltration.

Box 5.4

Contamination of pervious surfaces may vary from low levels of continuous contamination, such as droplets of oil from vehicles in car parks, to the sudden spillage of large quantities of a pollutant brought on to the surface on one occasion. It is important that all such possibilities are considered in determining the level of protection to be provided against groundwater or surface water contamination. There are some locations that have an unacceptably high risk of generating contaminated runoff or where the groundwater is an important resource. These are known as stormwater hotspots (Centre for Watershed Protection, 2000), where pervious surfaces should normally have a fully sealed base to prevent infiltration (Box 5.4).

Box 5.4   *Stormwater hotspots*

The Centre for Watershed Protection (2000) defines stormwater hotspots as areas where:

- land use or activities can potentially generate highly contaminated runoff
- groundwater is an important source for drinking water abstraction.

Such areas are defined by three factors.

Groundwater resource value
In areas such as groundwater source protection zones only fully tanked systems should be used. Outflow should be via pipes to surface water sewers or watercourses.

Use of site
Locations include:

- fuel stations
- hazardous or toxic materials storage or handling areas
- vehicle or equipment maintenance areas.

Pervious surfaces should not normally be used in these locations unless a full assessment of the risks and consequences of both general day-to-day and major spillage has been undertaken. A fully tanked system should be used with a mechanism for closing the outlet from the system provided.

Such sites can also be subdivided into separate catchments so that low-risk areas can be drained with pervious surfaces. For example, supermarkets can have pervious surfaces below car parks and conventional surfacing and drainage with interceptors in loading bays or other higher-risk areas.

Ground conditions
On sites where contaminated soils are present pervious pavements should normally have a fully sealed base to prevent infiltration. Where ground contamination is minor, and is not mobile, infiltration may be possible if a risk assessment identifies that risks to groundwater are acceptable.

5.4   WATER QUALITY ENHANCEMENT

There is no documented case where the use of pervious surfaces has been found to cause a deterioration in the quality of receiving waters. All the evidence to date has demonstrated an improvement in water quality. Pervious surfaces can be designed to provide various interception mechanisms that mitigate against the risks posed to controlled waters. Available methods include:

- filtration
- biodegradation of organic pollutants, such as petrol and diesel
- adsorption of pollutants (pollutants attach or bind to surfaces within the construction), which depends on factors such as texture, aggregate structure and moisture content
- settlement and retention of solids
- use of sealed bases to prevent infiltration to groundwater

- use of additional treatment methods at the outflow from the pervious surface, such as wetlands or lagoons (see CIRIA Report 142 (Luker and Montague, 1994))

- use of enhanced soils to improve treatment within the pervious pavement system. This can be achieved using either proprietary systems or by the addition of small amounts of substrate or materials with a high adsorption capacity to conventional aggregates (sawdust, peat, clay soils, granular activated carbon can all increase adsorption). The additional materials should not reduce the structural or hydraulic performance of the aggregates. The required microbes are usually already present in the ground and additional applications of microbes are not required.

The use of pervious surfaces should also give a benefit to water quality as a result of reduction in peak flows to receiving waters, which enhances the settlement and biodegradation of pollutants. Where the outflow is released to surface waters the reduced peak flow causes less of a short-term shock pollutant load to the receiving waters and allows increased dilution. This is generally an improvement over traditional systems where the first-flush effect can be pronounced (see Section 3.1). The delay and treatment provided by pervious systems can attenuate this effect.

5.4.1 Filtration

Pollutants that are conveyed in association with sediment, may be filtered from the percolating waters. This may occur through trapping within the soil or aggregate matrix, or on geotextile layers within the construction. Alternatively, as the interior of some types of pervious structure has an extensive system of voids, flow velocities may be reduced, leading to the deposition of material. The location of any filtration and/or sedimentation depends upon the internal structure of the pervious surface, for example whether a geotextile layer is near the surface or at the subgrade.

Sand filters are used at the base of pervious pavements in the USA where filtration before infiltration into the ground is required. Guidance on the design of filtration systems is given by Clayton and Schueler (1996).

5.4.2 Adsorption

Adsorption occurs when pollutants attach or bind to the surface of soil or aggregate particles. The actual process is complex but tends to be a combination of surface reactions grouped as sorption processes:

- adsorption – pollutants bind to surface of soil/aggregate
- cation exchange – attraction between cations and clay minerals
- chemisorption – solute is incorporated in the structure of a soil/aggregate
- absorption – the solute diffuses into the soil/aggregate/organic matter.

Realistically, it is impossible to separate these processes in a pervious pavement system.

The acidity of the water passing through the structure may be changed by contact with the construction materials. Acid rainfall (pH 6.0) intercepted by small elemental concrete block permeable surfacing with granite aggregate below has been observed to discharge effluent of neutral acidity (Pratt, 1995). This change in acidity may encourage the adsorption of pollutants by construction materials or by silt and sediment being transported, which may be filtered or deposited. The through-flow of water and pollutants may be interrupted by temporary storage in hollows in the construction materials, by surface tension and by trapping behind blockages of accumulated material. Any delay provides the opportunity for chemical or biological processes to occur, which may retain or degrade pollutants.

Eventually the materials onto which pollutants adsorb will become saturated, causing this method of treatment to stop. It is possible to estimate the maximum capacity of materials to adsorb contaminants using techniques adopted for design of contaminated water treatment plants (Muhammad *et al*, 1998, and US Army Corps of Engineers, 2001). The process depends on the precise combination and concentration of pollutants, so laboratory testing should be undertaken on a site-specific basis. This allows the design life of the pavement's capacity for pollutant adsorption to be estimated.

5.4.3 Biodegradation

In addition to the physical and chemical processes, which may occur on and within a pervious pavement, biological treatment may also take place. Microbial communities may be established within the structure, using the oxygen within the free-draining materials and the nutrients supplied with the inflows, to degrade organic pollutants such as oils and grease. The level of activity of such bio-remediation will be affected by the environmental conditions such as temperature and the supply of oxygen and nutrients. It also depends on the physical conditions within the structure such as the suitability of the materials for colonisation.

5.4.4 Storage

While not itself a treatment process, pollutants may be stored in the pervious structure, if appropriately designed, through the coating of the materials or the filling of voids and allowing for additional appropriate treatment at a later date. An example of this might be the storage of waters within a pervious car park previously used by the fire brigade to extinguish an adjacent building on fire. Such fire waters may convey all sorts of pollutants according to the property usage. If these are allowed to enter a watercourse much harm could be caused, as the waters would be difficult to contain and treat.

5.4.5 Complementary treatment methods

Dissolved pollutants not treated or adsorbed in the pervious pavement will pass to the base of the construction where infiltration to the soil may be possible, if the risk to groundwater is acceptable and there is sufficient thickness of unsaturated zone. Percolation through the upper soil horizons may provide some opportunities for further treatment of pollutants, which limits their forward movement to groundwater. Treatment is most effective in soil layers rich in organic matter, which may well have been removed as part of the construction process. Evidence (Section 5.5 and Appendix A6) suggests that a 1 m thickness of soil is sufficient to prevent downward migration of the common contaminants in the percolating water. The thickness of the unsaturated zone and rate of infiltration should be considered when assessing this method of treatment. The risk to groundwater if the design assumptions are incorrect means that a cautious approach should be adopted.

The accumulation of silt and sediment at the base of the construction may provide a further organic-rich layer of material providing treatment after some years of operation.

In sensitive locations, where additional reassurance is required that pollution of surface waters will not occur, additional treatment methods can be used at the outflow from pervious surfaces that are undersealed to prevent infiltration. Commonly used methods from conventional drainage systems include wetlands, lagoons and storage ponds. These have the advantage that they can be more easily maintained if they become saturated with pollutants. The use of such a secondary treatment system also means that if a pervious surface becomes saturated with pollutants, providing it is still operating in other respects, it should be able to remain in place. Detailed guidance is provided in CIRIA Report 142 (Luker and Montague, 1994).

5.4.6 Summary of quality enhancement options

Pervious surfaces and their underlying structures provide mechanisms that encourage filtration, sedimentation, adsorption, chemical/biological treatment and storage. The local nature of the surface water inflows means that such flows are limited in magnitude and velocity, which improves the effectiveness of these treatment processes. If necessary, additional treatment can be provided at the outlet from the pervious pavement structure. This *treatment train* approach also offers the best opportunity to provide some form of treatment for the range of pollutants present in the environment, conveyed by surface water runoff.

5.5 REVIEW OF PERFORMANCE REPORTED IN THE LITERATURE

Pollution is deposited on pavements as a result of the action of wind and rainfall, through the passage of people and vehicles over them and the activities for which they are used. The major benefit of pervious pavements, as compared with traditional impermeable ones, is their ability to reduce the concentration of pollutants discharged within the waters leaving the pavements.

Two mechanisms reduce the concentrations of pollutants discharged (Day *et al*, 1981 and Pratt *et al*, 1995).

1. Pollutants are retained within the pervious construction, physically trapped or adsorbed on materials.

2. And/or the volume of water discharged is reduced, hence the mass of pollutant being conveyed is itself reduced at any given concentration.

The pollutants are trapped within the construction at various locations according to the type of pervious construction. In cases where a geotextile is installed, much of the pollution is retained on it. In some cases the geotextile is situated in the upper layers of the construction (as with porous/permeable concrete block surfacing bedded on gravel); in others it is used as a separation layer at the subgrade. In both situations field and laboratory studies have reported the concentration of pollutants on the geotextile (Hogland, 1990; Legret *et al*, 1998; Schofield, 1994) (see Appendix A6).

The transport of pollutants out of the base of pervious pavements into the underlying soil has not been directly measured. Investigations of the pollutants retained below soakaways in Switzerland (Mikkelsen *et al*, 1997) and at Brandon, Suffolk (Pratt, 1996), have shown that much is retained within 500 mm of the base of the soakaway. The pollutants retained in this depth of soil were associated with silt and sediments washed into the soakaways, which were then trapped by the soil. Dissolved pollutants will pass directly through infiltration devices, with the threat of groundwater contamination. If the risks to groundwater are considered unacceptable, or the pervious constructions are located in a stormwater hotspot (Box 5.4), infiltration should not be allowed and outflow should be by a pipe conveyed to an outfall.

Besides trapping some pollutants, some types of pervious construction can hasten degradation by micro-organisms of trapped oils (Pratt, 1999). When located in the upper layers of the construction, the geotextile was found to retain 60–90 per cent of the oil entering the construction, with some 99 per cent of the oil being trapped in the construction as a whole over a four-year period. In a laboratory experiment, the degradation of the stored oil was monitored and found to take one to two years. It was estimated that it would take more than 100 years to saturate this type of pervious construction with oil, even at an inflow concentration of 1800 mg/l and at the observed rate of degradation. Oil saturation of the pavement is not seen as a problem, therefore, where supply is evenly spread over time. A major oil spill would necessitate the closure of an outlet drain, assuming an impermeable underseal, and significant remedial works. As with dissolved pollutants it is advisable to underseal pervious surfaces where potential for harm exists and to provide for monitoring and prevention of discharge, where required. More details of the effects of pervious pavements on water quality are provided in Appendix A6.

5.6 DESIGN, CONSTRUCTION AND MAINTENANCE IMPLICATIONS

Information gained from field and laboratory experience shows that, to ensure effective pollution control of surface water, various design features and operational procedures are required on pervious surfaces and their substructures. A pervious pavement is a treatment train and not a single pollution control mechanism. This means that the following factors must be considered:

- most importantly, the effectiveness of an infiltration system in preventing pollutants from entering the groundwater. This requires positioning the system well above the groundwater – the Environment Agency generally requires a minimum depth of 1 m between the base of a soakaway and the maximum groundwater level. This also seems reasonable for pervious pavement systems. This should, however, be confirmed with the relevant authority for a particular site

- the pervious surface and the mechanisms of pollutant entry

- the immediate substructure supporting the pervious surface and its ability to trap pollutants over the life of the pavement

- the remaining layer(s) of the construction and their ability to establish and sustain chemical and biological processes for the treatment of pollutants over the life of the pavement

- the base of the construction, which may be a storage zone for pollutants, from where discharge takes place to an external drainage system or to the soil and groundwater

- the risk of accidental spillage must be considered and the consequences of such events assessed and where necessary mitigated against (Box 5.1)

- the evidence suggests that the outflow from permeable pavements will generally be expected to be of a better quality than that from conventional drainage systems.

5.6.1 Pervious surface

Sediment-associated pollutants, together with silt and sediment themselves, will enter inlets and pore spaces on the surface with the potential to cause clogging. Mechanical cleansing of blockages is possible, although not particularly effective in the long term. Care must be exercised that any pollutant-enriched waters used in any flushing process are collected, removed and disposed of in accordance with waste management legislation (Box 3.8).

Unless pollutants are visible on the surface, such as sediment or hydrocarbon staining, they are unlikely to initiate maintenance or remedial work. Sediment deposits result in surface ponding and usually receive attention and should be disposed of with appropriate care (see Box 3.8). Remedial works are unlikely to be completed without some percolation of cleaning fluids, with consequent impacts on the internal pollution-control operations of the pavement substructure and, potentially, to the receiving waters of the outflow from the pavement.

5.6.2 Surface substructure

Positioning a geotextile near the surface of the pervious construction should enable pollutants to be trapped and retained close to the surface of the construction. This retention has disadvantages and advantages. The main disadvantage is that the filtering of sediments and their associated pollutants at this level may hamper percolation of waters and can eventually lead to surface ponding. A benefit is that even if eventual maintenance is required to reinstate infiltration, only a limited amount of the construction needs to be disturbed, since the sub-base below the geotextile is protected. While this is true for all pervious surfaces it is less convenient and economic with pervious surfaces that are continuous-laid, as the surfacing cannot be reused. The quantity of polluted material is generally limited. In addition, the pollutant concentration at a high level in the structure allows for its release over time. It is slowly transported in the stormwater to lower levels where chemical and biological processes may be operating to retain or degrade pollutants.

To assist with pollution control, it is helpful to include a geotextile in the upper layers of the pavement. The design should ensure that sufficient void space exists for the storage of sediments to limit the period between remedial works. This can be estimated by considering the filter criteria of the geotextile (Box 6.1) and the quantity and grain size distribution of sediment in the water entering the pervious surface (Luker and Montague, 1994).

5.6.3 Remaining layers of construction

These layers represent the site of long-term chemical and biological pollutant retention and degradation processes. Construction materials should be selected not only for their structural strength properties but also for their ability to sustain such processes. In general, this means that materials should create neutral or slightly alkaline conditions and they should provide favourable sites for colonisation by microbial populations. Materials could range from natural soils to man-made plastic, load-bearing void-formers. The structure formed of the material should be open-textured to facilitate drainage and aeration, but should ideally have sites where percolating waters may be ponded or held by surface tension, thus delaying through-flow.

5.6.4 Base of the construction

The interface between the base of the construction and the soil is an important structural element because of the effect of both the loading and the presence of water on the bearing capacity of the soil. Where granular materials are placed upon the soil at the base of a construction, a geotextile separating layer is often installed to prevent soil ingress and aggregate penetration of the subgrade. This geotextile is also important for pollution retention, as it encourages the accumulation of silts and sediment, which assist in the further retention of pollutants. This sludge accumulation should be encouraged and planned for within the design, although its removal is not expected to be part of general maintenance. It will be a consideration at the decommissioning of the pavement if the land is to be put to alternative uses.

Ground conditions may make infiltration through the base of the pavement unacceptable, in which case an impermeable geomembrane should be placed below and around the sides of the construction and the substructure drained via one or more outlets to an appropriate outfall. There remain concerns about the passage of dissolved pollutants to groundwater, and a geomembrane liner should be used in all cases where the risk of groundwater pollution is deemed unacceptable. In any sensitive locations the drains from the structure should pass through a suitable chamber, fitted with a closure device to prevent discharge, and in which periodic sampling can be undertaken. Such a facility would assist in the development of knowledge of effluent quality at the site with its associated land use and human activities. Under such a quality management regime, the subsequent infiltration of the outflow outside the pavement might proceed with some assurance that the outflow was of acceptable quality in normal usage of the pervious surface.

5.6.5   Other considerations

The destination of potential, dissolved pollutants should be considered, as their interception must lead to improvements in receiving water quality. It may be necessary to include specific layers of enhanced soils or components within the construction, designed to absorb or treat such pollutants.

6 Recommended design methodolgy

6.1 DESIGN OBJECTIVES

It is important that the design objectives are clearly defined and agreed at the earliest possible stage taking into consideration the following criteria:

- site characteristics
- allowable discharge rates
- groundwater protection
- geological sensitivities
- environmental issues
- type of application
- success/failure criteria
- aesthetic requirements
- maintenance implications.

What is the purpose of the pavement?

- to infiltrate water into the subgrade for disposal or to maintain soil moisture content
- to attenuate surface water runoff within the sub-base for flow control
- to attenuate surface water runoff within the sub-base for reuse
- to provide an erosion-protected surface
- to provide treatment to surface water runoff before disposal
- to remove or reduce costs of positive drainage for the site.

What surface finish is required?

- smooth finishes for medium and heavy traffic loading, trolleys, wheelchairs, footpaths
- rough finishes for light traffic loads (such as car parks), green areas or landscaping.

What type of sub-base should be used?
This depends on:

- the voids ratio required to provide the attenuation volume
- the strength requirements for the loading conditions.

Can surface water runoff be allowed to infiltrate the sub-grade? This depends on whether:

- risk assessment shows acceptable risk to groundwater and infiltration meets Environment Agency criteria
- the strength of the subgrade will decrease with frequent wetting over time
- the subgrade contains materials that decompose or change volume
- there is a likelihood that water in the subgrade will flow towards building or road foundations less than 5 m away
- the surface water runoff may contain pollutants that should not enter the soil
- the depth to the water table is acceptable
- the subgrade contains pollutants that might be mobilised by infiltration and enter the groundwater.

6.2 INFORMATION REVIEW AND CHECKLIST

The information review element of the design process should follow the recommended format in Appendix A3, which should minimise the risk of overlooking relevant data. It will also assist in the assessment of the selection criteria to establish the viable options of pervious pavement types on a project-specific basis. A basic checklist of required information, such as the one in Appendix A3, will assist in the development of a standardised approach in the review process.

6.3 RECOMMENDED DESIGN METHODOLOGY

The general procedure in Figure 6.1 should be adopted when undertaking conceptual/ detailed designs of pervious pavements.

Care must also be taken when programming construction works where pervious surfaces are to be installed. They should be protected from site traffic after installation, otherwise they can become easily clogged with mud and other debris from site. The site staff should be made aware of the presence of the pervious surface and how it works to avoid, for example, geotextiles being omitted or placed in the wrong location within the system.

6.4 DESIGN AND SPECIFICATION AND VALIDATION OF MATERIALS/COMPONENTS

The correct specification of materials/components is critical to the success of the system at the installation and through life stages. As discussed previously the use of performance-based specifications will minimise the risk of sub-standard materials and installation methods being used. The assessment and approval of materials should be based upon independently derived validation data to substantiate the information provided by the manufacturer/distributor. This is particularly relevant in the case of geosynthetics due to a lack of independent recognised standards and test protocols.

The implementation of a comprehensive Construction Quality Assurance (CQA) regime is fundamental to the achievement of a minimum standard of workmanship. It is generally accepted that a high proportion of the perceived failures of pervious surfaces is a direct result of poor-quality workmanship at the installation stage.

Certain construction-related issues need to be considered at the design stage. In particular, the local availability of the selected grading of granular materials can seriously affect the technical and commercial viability of the system. Further information on the issues to be considered when deriving whole-life costs is provided in Appendix A5.

Figure 6.1

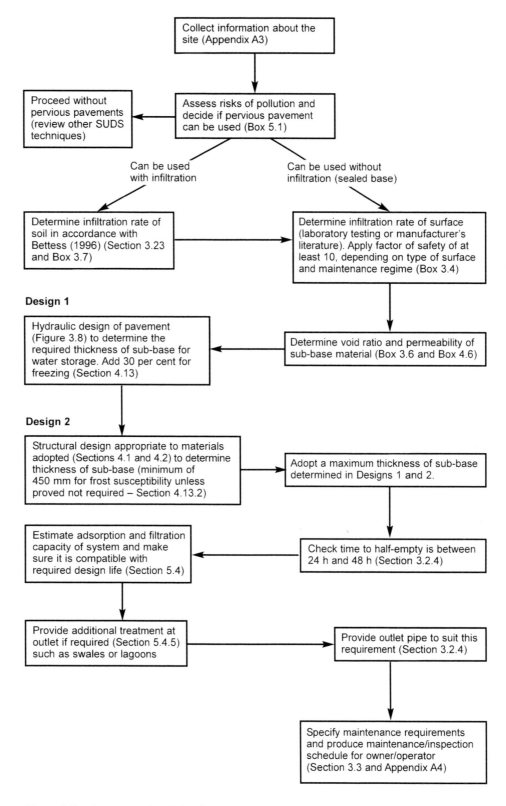

Figure 6.1 *Recommended design flow chart*

6.4.1　Geotextiles

Geotextile layers are an important element in pervious pavement systems both as a filtration layer below the pervious surface (Chapter 5) and as a separation layer at the interface between the base of the construction and subgrade soils (Section 4.8). Designers need to take careful consideration of geotextile properties with respect to the selection and specification of geotextiles. Many designers refer to layers within the construction that require specific properties merely as "geotextiles". The variability in performance of commercially available geotextiles is vast. They can vary in thickness from a few microns to tens of millimetres, can be manufactured from a diverse range of raw material (eg polyethylene, polypropylene, polyesters) and be any blend of the foregoing with various mixtures of virgin or recycled material. Geotextiles can be woven, non-woven, needle-punched or thermally bonded, all with different pore sizes and permeability.

All these aspects give rise to a huge variance with regard to physical properties and performance of geotextiles, together with UV resistance, durability and robustness during installation. All too often designers specify a geotextile based on a popular brand name alone without due consideration of the required material properties.

Important aspects to consider for geotextiles used in pervious pavements are:

- pore size. The pore size should be designed and specified to assist in filtration and prevent migration of fine soil particles. This can be achieved using equations in Box 6.1.

- permeability and breakthrough head. The geotextile should not limit flow of water in the system. It should therefore have a similar or greater permeability than the surrounding materials. With certain thermally bonded geotextiles an initial head of water is required before the geotextile will allow fluids to pass through. This is known as the "breakthrough head". In practice, this means that if a designer specifies a "geotextile layer" requiring filtration capabilities, at a distance of typically 130 mm beneath the surface layer of a pervious block paved surface, the contractor can quite easily install a thermally bonded geotextile. If, however, the breakthrough head for the geotextile selected is 200 mm, flooding will occur to a depth of 70 mm before infiltration through the geotextile takes place.

- puncture resistance. The geotextile must be able to resist the punching stresses caused by loading on sharp points of contact.

- tensile strength. The geotextile must have sufficient strength to resist the imposed forces from traffic or other loading.

Box 6.1 *Recommended geotextile filter criteria*

Many criteria have been defined for geotextile filter design. Most are similar and use the upstream soil particle size characteristic and compare it to the O_{95} of the geotextile. The American Association of State Highway and Transportation Officials (AASHTO, 1990) has developed a simple criterion, as below.

For soils < 50 per cent passing 75 micron sieve

$$O_{95} < 0.59 \text{ mm} \quad \text{(ie, apparent opening size } (AOS)_{fabric} > 600 \text{ micron)}$$

For soils > 50 per cent passing 75 micron sieve

$$O_{95} < 0.3 \text{ mm} \quad \text{(ie, apparent opening size } (AOS)_{fabric} > 300 \text{ micron)}$$

O_{95} is the geotextile pore size opening for which 95 per cent of the holes are smaller.

AOS is the largest soil particle that would effectively pass through the geotextile.

An alternative method is to compare geotextile opening sizes directly to a soil particle size. Carroll (1983) proposed:

$$O_{95} < (2 \text{ or } 3) D_{85}$$

D_{85} is the soil particle size in mm for which 85 per cent of the soil is finer.

Many others have been proposed according to the geotextile type, soil type, flow regime etc.

---

continued on next page...

Box 6.1   *Recommended geotextile filter criteria*

The US Federal Highway Administration (FHWA) gives the following requirements (Holtz *et al*, 1995).

For fine-grained soils > 50 per cent passing 75 micron sieve

Woven geotextiles – apparent opening size $(AOS)_{fabric} < D_{85}$

Non-woven geotextiles – apparent opening size $(AOS)_{fabric} < 0.3$ mm or
> 300 micron apparent opening size $(AOS)_{fabric} < 1.8 D_{85 \, soil}$

For granular soils < 50 per cent passing 75 micron sieve

All geotextiles – apparent opening size $(AOS)_{fabric} < B \times D_{85 \, soil}$

Where:
B = 1 for $2 > C_u > 8$
B = 0.5 for $2 < C_u < 4$
B = $8/C_u$ for $4 < C_u < 8$

and $C_u = D_{60}/D_{10}$ (ie uniformity coefficient)

6.4.2   Impermeable geomembranes

Care should be taken when specifying and selecting an impermeable geomembrane to the base and sides of pavement structures for which infiltration techniques are unacceptable. This is critical if the impermeable geomembrane is providing protection to sensitive aquifers beneath. The material specified for an impermeable geomembrane must be able to withstand the rigours of installation and possess the physical characteristics to resist:

- puncture
- multi-axial elongation stress and strains associated with settlement
- environmental stress cracking and remain intact for the design life.

It is essential to seal the joints between adjacent sheets of impermeable geomembranes correctly. Geomembranes designed to be impermeable should be seamed using proprietary welding techniques. The integrity of joints is just as important as the selection of the geomembrane. For example, a correctly specified geomembrane would not be fit for purpose if jointed with tape, as the integrity of the system would then rely on the mechanical properties of the tape. It is also important to be able to demonstrate the integrity of joints by non-destructive testing. Advice on seam testing is given in CIRIA Report 124 (Privett *et al*, 1996).

It is recommended that heavy-duty geotextiles be placed both above and below the geomembrane to provide further assurance of the integrity of the installed systems. Also, a comprehensive construction quality assurance (CQA) protocol should be in place during the construction phase of the works. It should include, as a minimum, material delivery inventories, documented storage conditions, non-destructive seam-testing results and visual inspection reports for each element of the system during the installation of the components.

6.5   DESIGN TOOLS

Historically, the industry has relied on guidance provided by the manufacturers/distributors of proprietary systems for the correct approach to the design process. While this information is of great value once a particular system has been selected, the available advice is typically system-specific and is of limited value in the selection process.

Manufacturers/distributors are providing increasing levels of support at the design stage including the option of a "full" design service incorporating project-specific design liability.

Proprietary drainage software specialists are beginning to develop source control programmes, which in varying degrees take into consideration the hydraulic performance of a system. The software is limited, however, as it does not take into consideration the lateral flow through layers directly beneath the surfacing, which has an impact on storage volumes, surface flooding and discharge rates.

6.6   HEALTH AND SAFETY

When designed correctly, pervious pavements should not present a significant risk to health and safety. Benefits over conventional pavements and drainage systems include:

- reduced use of manholes and associated heavy covers located in traffic areas. Manholes are also dangerous confined spaces
- reduced use of gullies and kerbs (potential trip hazards)
- fewer routes for vermin to enter pipe systems, thus reducing the risk of diseases such as leptospirosis, which can occur when rats are active.

There are no specific risks associated with construction and maintenance of pervious surfaces over and above those that apply to conventional pavements. A risk assessment for any pervious pavement design should be undertaken at the feasibility or design stage, in accordance with the Construction (Design and Management) Regulations, 1994.

6.7   ADOPTION

The issues of adoption, ownership and responsibility of sustainable drainage systems are being reviewed by the national SUDS working parties (led by the Environment Agency and SEPA). They are working to resolve these issues and provide guidance to simplify adoption of the systems.

The adoption issues associated with pervious surfaces are discussed in more detail in Appendix A7.

REFERENCES

Abbott C L, Comino L and Angood C (2000) *Monitoring performance of infiltration drainage systems*, Report SR569, HR Wallingford Ltd

American Association of State Highway and Transportation Officials (1990) *AASHTO-AGC-ARTBA Joint Committee. Guide specifications and test procedures for geotextile*, Task Force 25 Report, Washington DC

American Society of Testing Materials (2001) *Specification for concrete aggregates* ASTM C33-01a

Australian Water Technologies (1999) *Powells Creek East Catchment stormwater quality scheme*, Report for Concord Council, New South Wales, Australia. AWT Environment, Science and Technology, ref 1999/0359

Austroads (1992) *A guide to the structural design of pavements*, Publication AP-17/92, Sydney

Bettess R (1996) *Infiltration drainage, manual of good practice*, Report 156 Construction Industry Research and Information Association, London

Bond P C, Pratt C J and Newman A P (1999) *A review of stormwater quantity and quality performance of permeable pavements in the UK*, Proc 8th Int Conf on Urban Storm Drainage, Sydney, Australia, pp 248–255

Boon C (2000) *Modelling and monitoring the performance of a sustainable urban drainage system – porous pavement*, unpublished MSc thesis, University of Abertay, Dundee

Boussinesq J (1885) *Application des potentiels a l'étude de l'équilibre et des mouvements des solides élastiques*, Gauthier-Villars, Paris

British Standards Institution (1973) *Code of practice for plastics pipework (thermoplastic materials). General principles and choice of material*, BS 312: Part 1: 1973, BSI

British Standards Institution (1983) *Specification for air cooled blast furnace slag aggregate for use in construction*, BS 1047:1983, BSI

British Standards Institution (1989) *Testing aggregates. Method for determination of particle shape – flakiness index*, BS 812: Section 105.1: 1989, BSI

British Standards Institution (1989) *Test method for determination of frost heave*, BS 812: Part 124: 1989, BSI

British Standards Institution (1990) *Testing aggregates Methods for determination of 10% fines value*, BS 812:Part 111 :1990, BSI.

British Standards Institution (1990) *Methods of tests for soils for civil engineering purposes: Part 4 Compaction Tests*. BS 1377: Part 4: 1990, BSI

British Standards Institution (1990) *Methods of tests for soils for civil engineering purposes: Part 9 In-situ Test*, BS 1377: Part 9: 1990, BSI

British Standards Institution (1992) *Specification for aggregates from natural sources for concrete*, BS 882:1992, BSI

British Standards Institution (1997) *Structural use of concrete: Code of practice for design and construction*, BS 8110: Part 1: 1997, BSI.

British Standards Institution (2001) *Pavements constructed with clay, natural aggregate or concrete pavers – Part 1: Guide for the structural design of heavy duty pavements constructed of clay pavers or concrete paving blocks*, BS 7533-1: 2001, BSI

British Standards Institution (2001) *Pavements constructed with clay, natural aggregate or concrete pavers – Part 2: Guide for the structural design of lightly trafficked pavements constructed of clay pavers or concrete paving blocks*, BS 7533-2: 2001, BSI

British Standards Institution (2001) *Coated macadam (asphalt concrete) for roads and other paved areas – Part 1: Specification for constituent materials and for mixtures*, BS 4987-1:2001, BSI

Brown S and Brunton J (1984) Improvements to pavement subgrade strain criterion, *Journal of Transport Engineering*, ASCE, vol 110, no 6

Building Research Establishment (1991) Soakaway Design, *BRE Digest 365*, September 1991, Garston, England

Cahill T (2000) *A second look at porous pavement/underground recharge. The practice of watershed protection*, Article 103, Thomas R Schueler and Heather K Holland (eds), Centre for Watershed Protection, USA

Cao S L, Poduska D, and Zollinger D G (1998) *Drainage design and performance guidelines for Uni Eco-Aggregate permeable pavement*, Department of Civil Engineering, the Texas A&M University System, published by Uni-Group USA

Carpenter V (2000) *Bognor Regis Sports Centre – Case study of sustainable urban drainage systems*, Proc Standing Conf on Stormwater Source Control, Volume XIX, ISBN 0 905949 88 9

Carroll R G (1983) *Geotextile filter criteria*, TRR96, Engineering Fabrics in Transportation Construction, Washington DC, pp 46–53

Cedergren H R (1974) *Drainage of highway and airfield pavements*, Wiley Interscience

Centre for Watershed Protection (2000) *2000 Maryland stormwater design manual*, Volumes one and two, prepared by the Centre for Watershed Protection, Ellicott City, Maryland, USA on behalf of the Maryland Department of the Environment

CIRIA (1995) *Infiltration drainage – case studies of UK practice*, Project Report 22, Construction Industry Research and Information Association, London

CIRIA (2000a) *Sustainable urban drainage systems – design manual for Scotland and Northern Ireland*, C521, Construction Industry Research and Information Association, London

CIRIA (2000b) *Sustainable urban drainage systems – design manual for England and Wales*, C522, Construction Industry Research and Information Association, London

CIRIA (2001a) *Sustainable urban drainage systems – best practice manual*, C523, Construction Industry Research and Information Association, London

CIRIA (2001b) *Rainwater and greywater use in buildings – best practice guide*, C539, Construction Industry Research and Information Association, London

CIRIA (2001c) *Rainwater and greywater use in buildings – decision making for water conservation*, Project Report 80, Construction Industry Research and Information Association, London

Clayton R A and Schueler T R (1996) *Design of stormwater filtering systems*, Centre for Watershed Protection, Silver Spring, Maryland, USA

Coventry S, Woolveridge C and Hillier S (1999) *The reclaimed and recycled construction materials handbook*, C513, Construction Industry Research and Information Association, London

Day G E, Smith D R and Bowers J (1981) *Runoff and pollution abatement characteristics of concrete grid pavements*, Bulletin 135, Virginia Water Resources Research Centre, Virginia State University, USA

Department of the Environment in Northern Ireland (2001) *Policy and practice for the protection of groundwater in Northern Ireland*, Environment and Heritage Services, July 2001

Environment Agency (1998) *Policy and practice for the protection of groundwater*. The Stationery Office

Federal Register (1986), Toxicity Characteristics Leaching Procedure (TCLP) *Federal Register*, vol 51, no 216, pp 40643-40652.

Fenner R A (2001) *Is urban drainage sustainable without improving maintenance?* Proc first National Conference on Sustainable Drainage, Coventry University, UK, 18–19 June 2001, ISBN 1 903818 06 0, pp 81–92

Hall M J, Hockin D L and Ellis J B (1993) *Design of flood storage reservoirs*, Book 14, Construction Industry Research and Information Association, London

Hazen A (1911) Discussion of dams on sand foundations. *Transactions*, no 73, American Society of Civil Engineers, New York

Highlands K L and Hoffman G L (1988) *Sub-base permeability and pavement performance*, Transportation Research Record 1159, TRB, National Research Council, Washington DC

Highways Agency, Scottish Executive, National Assembly for Wales and Department for Regional Development Northern Ireland (1992) *Design manual for roads and bridges*, Vol 7 with updates, HMSO, London

Highways Agency, Scottish Executive, National Assembly for Wales and Department for Regional Development Northern Ireland (1998) *Manual of contract documents for highway works. Vol. 1: Specification for highway works*, Stationery Office, London

Hogland W, Larson M and Berndtsson R (1990) *The pollutant build-up in pervious road construction*. Proc Fifth Int Conf on Urban Storm Drainage, Osaka, Japan pp 845–852

Holtz R D *et al* (1995) *Geosynthetic design and construction guidelines – participant notebook*, Federal Highway Administration Contract No FHWADTFH61-93-C-00120 McLean Virginia, 1995

Ingold T S (1994) *The geotextiles and geomembranes manual*, 1st edn, Elselvier Advanced Technology

Institute of Hydrology (1975) *Flood Studies Report*

Institute of Hydrology (1999) *Flood Estimation Handbook*

Jacobson P and Harremoes P (1981) *Significance of semi-pervious surfaces in urban hydrology*, Proc 2nd Int Conf on Urban Storm Drainage. ISBN 0918334 47 0 pp 424–433

Jewell R A (1996) *Soil reinforcement with geotextiles*, Special Publication 123, Construction Industry Research and Information Association, London

Kazmierowski T J A, Bradbury A and Hajek J (1994) *Field evaluation of various types of open graded drainage layers*, Transportation Research Record 1434, TRB National Research Council, Washington DC

Kipkie C W (1998) *Feasibility of a permeable pavement option in the storm water management model (SWMM) for long term continuous modelling*, Master of science thesis, University of Guelph, Canada

Knapton J (1976) *The design of concrete block roads. Cement and Concrete Association*, Wrexham Springs, Publication 42.545

Knapton J (1989) *Structural design of pavements surfaced with concrete blocks and clay pavers*, Proceedings of the 10th National Workshop, Institution of Highways and Transportation, Leamington Spa

Knapton J and Meletiou M (1996) *The structural design of heavy duty pavements for ports and other industries*, 3rd edn, British Precast Concrete Federation Limited, published on behalf of Interpave, London

Knapton J (2002) Interpave – A guide to the application of concrete block paving in permeable pavement, Interpave

Legret M, Nicollet M, Miloda P, Colandini V and Raimbault G (1998) *Simulation of heavy metal pollution from stormwater infiltration through a porous pavement with reservoir structure*, Proc 3rd Int Conf on Innovative Technologies in Urban Storm Drainage, Vol 1, pp 509–516

Lewin K, Bradshaw K, Blakey N C, Turrell J, Hennings S M and Flavin R J (1994) *Leaching tests for the assessment of contaminated land: Interim NRA Guidance*, National Rivers Authority, R&D Note 301, Bristol, UK

Luker M and Montague K (1994) *Control of pollution from highway drainage discharges*, Report 142, Construction Industry Research and Information Association, London

Macdonald K and Jefferies C (2001) *Performance comparison of porous paved and traditional car parks*, Proc 1st Nat Conf on Sustainable Drainage, Coventry University, ISBN 1 903818 06 0, pp 170–181

Mantle J D G (1993) *On-site reduction and attenuation of urban stormwater runoff*, unpublished PhD thesis, Nottingham Trent University

Mayhew H C and Harding H M (1987) *Thickness of concrete roads*, TRRL Research Report 87, Transport and Road Research Laboratory

Mikkelsen P S, Hafliger M, Ochs M, Jacobsen P, Tjell J C and Boller M (1997) *Pollution of soil and groundwater from infiltration of highly contaminated stormwater – a case study*, Water Science and Technology, vol 36, no 8–9, pp 325–330

Mitchell J K, Kao T C and Kavazanjian E (1979) *Analysis of grid cell reinforced pavement bases*, Report No GL-79-8, Geotechnical Laboratory, US Army Engineer Waterways Experiment Station, Vicksburg, MS, July 1979

Moulton L K (1980) *Highway subdrainage design*, Report FHWA-TS-80-224, August 1980, Federal Highways Administration

Muhammad N, Parr J, Smith M D and Wheatley A D (1998) *Adsorption of heavy metals in slow sand filters*. 24th WEDC Conference, Islamabad, 1998, Water, Engineering and Development Centre, Loughborough University

National House Building Council (1999) *National House Building Council Standards* Volume 4, Chapter 4.2, "Building Near Trees", NHBC

National Water Council and Department of the Environment (1981) *Design and analysis of urban storm drainage: The Wallingford Procedure, Volume 1: Principles, methods and practice*, NWC, London

New Civil Engineer (2002) New porous asphalt protects windscreens from flying stones, *New Civil Engineer*, 2 May 2002, p 11, Emap Construct Limited

Newman A P, Pratt C J, Coupe S J and Cresswell N (2001) *Oil bio-degradation in permeable pavements by inoculated and indigenous communities*, Proc 4th Int Conf on Innovative Technologies in Urban Storm Drainage, Lyon, France

Nicholls J C (1997) *Review of UK porous asphalt trials*, Transport Research Laboratory Report 264, HMSO

Portland Cement Association (1971) *Subgrades and sub-bases for concrete pavements*, TS 029.02

Potter J F and Halliday A R (1981) *Contribution of pervious macadam surfacing to structural performance in roads*, TRRL Laboratory Report LR 1022

Powell W D, Potter J F, Mayhew H C and Nunn M E (1984) *The Structural Design of Bituminous Roads*, Laboratory Report LR 1132, Transport and Road Research Laboratory

Pratt C J, Harrison J J, and Adams J R W (1984) *Storm runoff simulation in runoff quality investigations*. Proc 3rd Int conf on Urban Storm Drainage. ISBN 91 7032 128 0, pp 285–294

Pratt C J, Mantle J D G and Schofield P A (1995) *UK research into the performance of permeable reservoir structures in controlling stormwater discharge quantity and quality*. Proc 2nd Int Conf on Innovative Technologies in Urban Storm Drainage, Lyon, France. ISBN 2 9509337 0 X, pp 337–344

Pratt C J (1989) *Permeable pavements for stormwater quality enhancement*. Proc. ASCE Engineering Conf on Urban Stormwater Quality Enhancement – Source Control, Retrofitting and Combined Sewer Technology. Davos, Switzerland, pp 131–155

Pratt C J (1996) Research and development in methods of soakaway design, *Journal CIWEM*, Vol 10, pp 47–51

Pratt C J (1999) *Developments in permeable pavements: further observations on mineral oil bio-degradation*. Proc Standing Conf on Stormwater Source Control, Volume XVII, ISBN 0 905949 80 3

Privett K D, Mathews S C and Hodges R A (1996) *Barriers, liners and cover systems for containment and control of land contamination*, Special Publication 124, Construction Industry Research and Information Association

Quarry Products Association (2001) *Construction and surfacing of car parking areas including private drives*, Asphalt Information Service, Asphalt Applications 1 June 2001, Quarry Products Association

Road Research Laboratory (1952) *Soil Mechanics for Road Engineers*, Department of Scientific and Industrial Research, HMSO

Rollings R S and Rollings M P (1993) *Design considerations for the Uni Eco-stone concrete paver*, Uni Group USA, Florida

Rommel M, Rus M, Argue J, Johnson L and Pezzaniti D (2001) *Carpark with "1 to 1" (impervious/permeable) paving: performance of "Formpave" blocks*. Proc 4th Int Conf on Innovative Technologies in Urban Drainage, Lyon, France, ISBN 2 9509337 4 2, pp 807–814

Rudland D J, Lancefield R M and Mayell P N (2001) *Contaminated land risk assessment, a guide to good practice*, C552, Construction Industry Research and Information Association, London

Schluter W and Jefferies C (2001) *Monitoring the outflow from a porous car park*, Proc 1st Nat Conf on Sustainable Drainage, Coventry University, ISBN 1 903818 06 0, pp 182–191

Mcdonald K and Jefferies C (2001) *Performance comparison of porous paved and traditional car parks*, Proc 1st Nat Conf on Sustainable Drainage, Coventry. ISBN 1 903818 06 0, pp 170–181

Schofield P A (1994) *Urban stormwater quality improvement through the use of permeable pavements: the performance and potential of an experimental structure*, unpublished PhD thesis, Nottingham Trent University

Scott M A (2001) Personal communication, Coventry University

Scottish Environment Protection Agency (1996) *SEPA Policy No 1, Environment Act 1995*, Schedule 16 prohibition notices and discharges exempt from consent, May 1996 as amended May 2001

Scottish Environment Protection Agency (2000) SEPA Water Quality Classification Schemes. In: *West Region Water Quality Review*, interactive CD-rom

Scottish Environment Protection Agency (2001) *SEPA Policy No 15, Regulation of urban drainage*, May 2001

Scottish Environment Protection Agency and Environment Agency (1999) *Sustainable Urban Drainage, An Introduction, Protecting the quality of our environment*. Jointly published by SEPA and Environment Agency, ISBN 1 901322 12 8

Shackel B (1995) *Infiltration and the structural tests of Uni Eco-Loc and Uni Eco-stone paving*, School of Civil Engineering, University of New South Wales, Australia

Sheffield Metropolitan District Council (1998) *General Specification for Roads to be Adopted as Public Highways*, Planning, Transport and Highways, Adoptions Group, November 1998

Shell International Petroleum Company (1985) *Shell Pavement Design Manual*, London

Skrettegerg (1990) Private communication, Norwegian Water Resources Department

Smith D R (2001) *Permeable Interlocking Concrete Pavements, Selection, Design, Construction, Maintenance*, 2nd edn, Interlocking Concrete Pavement Institute, Washington DC

Taylor D (1948) *Fundamentals of soil mechanics*, John Wiley and Sons, New York

United States Army Corps of Engineers (2001) *Adsorption Design Guide*, Design Guide No 1110-1-2, Department of the Army, 1 March 2001

United States Environmental Protection Agency (1972) *Investigation of porous pavements for urban run off control*, Office of Research and Monitoring, Project no 11034 DUY, March 1972

United States Environmental Protection Agency (1980) *Porous pavement Phase 1 design and operational criteria*, Grant no R806338, EPA-600/2-80-135, August 1980

Wei, Irvine W (1986) *Installation and evaluation of permeable pavement at Walden Pond State Reservation*, Final Report 1986, North Eastern University, Department of Civil Engineering, Boston, Massachusetts

Woodman G (1992) *Failure Criteria for flexible pavements*, Property Services Agency Reports for British Airports Authority, Technical Services Division, Surrey UK

Appendices

A1 Case studies

1. Sports Centre, Bognor Regis, Sussex

2. National Air Traffic Services, Edinburgh

3. Royal Bank of Scotland, Edinburgh

4. Tesco, Wokingham, Berkshire

5. Wheatley Motorway Service Area, M40, Oxford

6. Powells Creek, Concord, New South Wales, Australia

CASE STUDY NO 1

Location	Bognor Regis, Sports Centre, car park

Lessons to be learned from this case study	Pervious surfaces can be successfully constructed over weak subgrades. They can also be constructed as infiltration systems where infiltration rates are low and they reduce peak outflows. Site trials of aggregates are useful to compare trafficability by construction plant.

Date of construction	Completed July 1999

Design philosophy	The site is underlain by Brickearth (clay) over raised beach deposits (clayey sand) over the Reading Formation (clay). Groundwater is around 1.2 m below ground level.

The local surface water sewer is shallow (requiring pumping from the site to reach it) and only 150 mm in diameter and unable to accept further flows.

A preliminary soils investigation included soakaway tests in accordance with BRE Digest 365. This was undertaken early to allow design of the drainage system. The infiltration rate measured was 2.3×10^{-6} m/s to 4.74×10^{-7} m/s, which would require large conventional soakaways. The formation was very weak, with a CBR value between 0.5 per cent and 1.7 per cent.

Because of the site constraints, a pervious surface for the car parking areas was adopted with infiltration from the base. The 300 m^2 car park accepted runoff from a total area of 2100 m^2, with storage below adjacent sports pitches.

The capital cost of the pervious car park solution was lower than other alternatives (see below).

Pervious car park – £149 000

Plastic boxes to form storage plus pumping to outfall – £169 000 + maintenance

Box culvert to form storage plus pumping to outfall – £184 000 + maintenance

Trench soakaways – £195 000

The hydraulic design is based on a 1 in 50-year rainfall event and was undertaken in accordance with BRE Digest 365, but with outflow through the base allowed.

The structural design was based on construction traffic loads that were more severe than the long-term light loads from car parking. Boussinesq's theory of stress distribution was used to assess the required pavement thickness. The sub-base was 570 mm thick and comprised Type C filter stone as specified in the *Specification for Highway Works*. (Note: Type C does not have a specified grading, but it should be well-graded, non-plastic and have a 10 per cent fines value greater than 50 kN.)

This was reinforced with a layer of geogrid at the base. The construction details are shown on Figures A1.1 and A1.2.

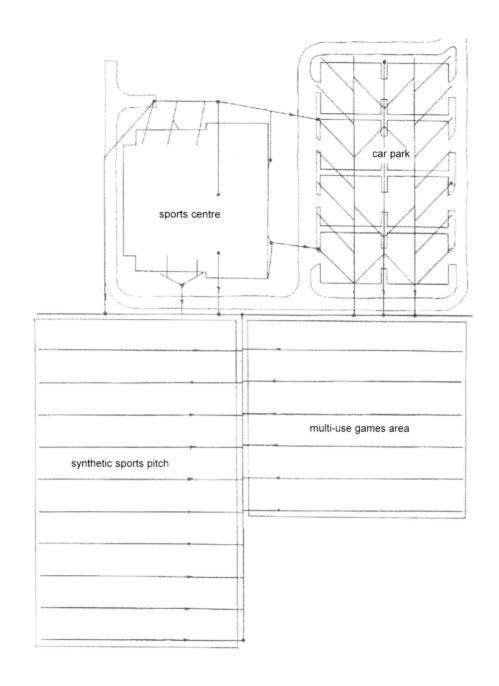

Figure A1.1 *Plan of drainage system (CIRIA, 2001a)*

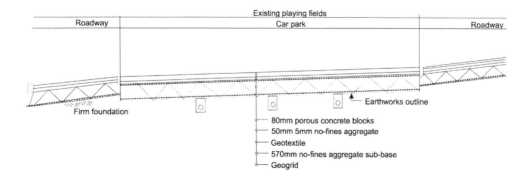

Figure A1.2 *Cross-section of pavement construction (Carpenter 2000)*

Maintenance	Maintenance includes regular vacuum sweeping; the cost of this was acceptable to the client. No other data on maintenance are available.
General comments	The information in this case study was obtained from Carpenter, 2000, Abbott *et al*, 2000 and CIRIA, 2001a. West Sussex County Council and the Environment Agency have proposed further monitoring of this site (see CIRIA, 2001a).

Hydraulic performance

No site flooding has been reported. Lmited monitoring of rainfall and water levels within the car park construction demonstrate that it is performing as required (Figure A1.3).

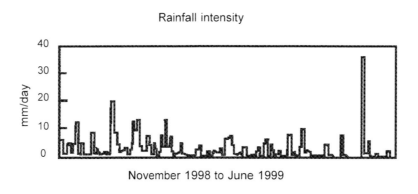

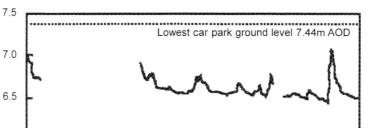

Figure A1.3 *Comparison of water levels in pavement to rainfall (Carpenter 2000)*

Water levels in car park construction compared to rainfall intensity

Infiltration tests were also undertaken on the pervious surface using an infiltrometer developed by the Transport Research Laboratory (TRL), shortly after construction. The results gave infiltration rates ranging from 230 mm/h to 4960 mm/h through the concrete blocks and between 1960 mm/h and 229 500 mm/h through the gaps between the concrete blocks themselves (Abbott *et al*, 2000).

Structural performance

There is no quantitative data but there are no reports of structural failure. The use of aggregate with a high voids ratio was initially perceived as problematic due to the difficulty in trafficking over it. This was overcome by site trials of aggregates from a variety of sources before construction.

Water quality performance

No data is available.

CASE STUDY NO 2

Location	National Air Traffic Services (NATS), Edinburgh, car park

Lessons to be learned from this case study	Pervious surfaces can successfully treat pollution washed off pervious surfaces by rainfall to reduce pollutant levels, and they can reduce both peak flows and the total volume of outflow significantly.

Date of construction	1996

| Design philosophy | Constructed as an extension to an existing impermeable car park. The underlying soil is a sandy clay. Although a geomembrane was not provided, infiltration is expected to be negligible due to the low permeability of the soil.

The construction comprises a permeable concrete block surface installed to the manufacturer's specification as shown in Figure A1.4. It comprises 80 mm block over a 50 mm bedding layer of 5 mm single-size gravel over a geotextile over 350 mm of sub-base: Type B filter material in accordance with the *Specification for Highway Works* with the following grading: |
|---|---|

Sieve size	percentage by mass passing
63 mm	100
37.5 mm	85–100
20 mm	0–25
10 mm	0–5

The material must also be non-plastic and have a 10 per cent fines value greater than 50 kN.

A perforated pipe in the sub-base acts as an overflow. The plan layout of the system is not available. The pervious pavement covers an area of 1401 m² and the impermeable area is 442 m².

Maintenance	Details of the maintenance regime are not available.

General comments	The information in this case study was obtained from Macdonald and Jefferies (2001) and from Kirsteen Macdonald at Ewan Association Limited in association with University of Abertay, Dundee.

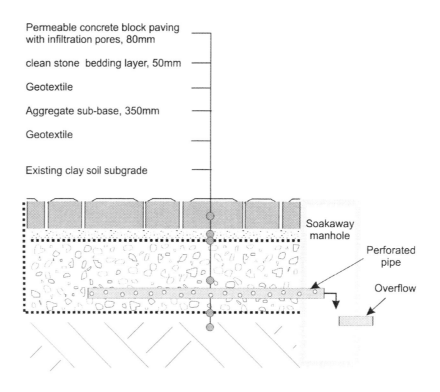

Figure A1.4 *Pavement construction at NATS, Edinburgh*

Hydraulic performance

Monitoring

Monitoring of both the impermeable and pervious surfaces was carried out between April 1998 and February 1999 and from February to May 2000. The pervious surface only was monitored between May and August 2000. In total, more than 150 rainfall events were recorded.

Results

The pervious pavement is shown to reduce peak flows and total volume of flow from the car park into the drainage system. A typical hydrograph is provided in Figure A1.5.

7th - 8th August 1998 (12:00 - 8:00)

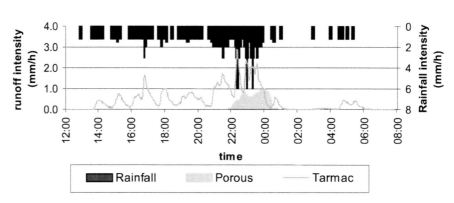

Figure A1.5 *Typical hydrograph at NATS (Macdonald and Jefferies, 2001)*

Outflow from the pervious surface varied between 0 per cent and 66 per cent, with a mean of 22.2 per cent depending on the duration and intensity of the rainfall event. This compares to values between 21.4 per cent and 72.8 per cent, with a mean of 48.2 per cent for the impermeable area. The reduction in peak flows from the pervious area compared with the impermeable area varied between 23.7 per cent and 98.4 per cent, with a mean of 76.8 per cent, and the lag time from the centroid of total rainfall to peak flow varied from 29 minutes to 600 minutes (average 180 minutes). This compared with values of -158 minutes to 123 minutes (average of 9.3 minutes) for the impermeable surface (negative values mean that the peak flow was before the centroid of total rainfall).

For the pervious surface, an average of 7.29 mm of rainfall was required before runoff began (range 2.6–17.2 mm) and for the conventional surface it was only 0.76 mm (range 0–26 mm).

Initial losses were also estimated for both surfaces and gave the following values for initial runoff loss (IRL):

> pervious surface IRL = 5.6 mm
> impermeable surface IRL = 0.8 mm.

Structural performance

There is no quantitative data on the structural performance of the car park, although no evidence of failure is reported.

Water quality performance

Water quality monitoring was undertaken for short periods during the hydraulic monitoring. The water from the pervious surface was monitored at the outlet manhole and the monitoring of the impermeable area was carried out at a gully pot. The results for the general water quality parameters are summarised in Tables A1.1 and A1.2.

Table A1.1 *General quality parameters results (Macdonald and Jefferies, 2001)*

Parameter[1]		Temperature °C	pH	Conductivity µS	Dissolved oxygen %	Turbidity NTU	Ammonium PPM
Average [2]	Impermeable	—	6.7	68	71	43	0.68
	Pervious	—	7.9	320	62.8	220	1.57
Range of EMCs	Impermeable	4.4–8.3	6.5–7	30.5–107	66–76	35.6–49.5	0.11–1.6
	Pervious	5.1–19.5	7.7–8.3	238–482	39.4–77	30–998	0.7–2.15
EMC reduction/increase (-/+)[3]		0.34	1.3	632%	+1.3%[4]	-24%	602%

Notes

1. Recorded by sonde (an automatic monitoring device) over 12 events.
2. Calculated from event mean concentration (EMC) for each event (except temperature and pH, which have no EMC, only average).
3. Calculated from reduction/increase for individual events, ie not the difference between the average.
4. From only one event.

Table A1.2 *General quality parameters results (Macdonald and Jefferies, 2001)*

Parameter[1]		pH	Conductivity µS/cm	TSS mg/l	BOD mg/l	TON mg/l	Ortho phos-phates mg/l	Chloride mg/l	Ammoniacal nitrogen mg/l
Average[2]	Impermeable	6.7	49.3	30.03	4.8	0.7	0.03	8.3	0.2
	Pervious	8	316.5	19.1	1.74	0.9	0.207	23.9	0.32
Range of EMCs	Impermeable	6.4–6.85	41–62	15.8–51	2.8–5.8	0.15–1.42	0.02–0.04	6.5–10.9	0.03–0.48
	Pervious	7.7–8.2	210–416	15–24	1.5–2.2	0.36–1.36	0.05–0.65	3–57.6	0.03–1.13
EMC reduction/increase (-/+)[3]		1.4	822%	-32%	-49%	165%	157.10%	397.80%	-32.60%

Notes

1. From laboratory analysis of samples taken by automatic sampler (six events and spot samples).
2. Calculated from EMC for each event (except pH, which has no EMC, only average).
3. Calculated from reduction/increase for individual events, ie not the difference between the average.

The results show variable improvements to water quality. The most significant results are the increased levels of conductivity, ammonium, total oxidised nitrogen (TON) and chloride from the pervious surface and reductions in turbidity and biochemical oxygen demand. The increase in TON and ammonium was attributed to possible decay of organic matter from plant debris within the pervious pavement. All the results for the pervious car park were, however, below the levels required for drinking water (Water Supply (Water Quality) Regulations 2000) where applicable.

The biochemical oxygen demand indicates the amount of oxygen used up by micro-organisms as they break down organic materials. The values recorded for the pervious car park are low compared with the EU Freshwater Fisheries Directive, which sets a maximum of 3 mg/l for salmonoid rivers. This indicates the water from the pervious car park can be considered clean. A river with these values would be classified as excellent quality by the Scottish Environment Protection Agency (SEPA, 2000).

The increase in conductivity was attributed to increased levels of chloride and dissolved solids, although the reason for this was not known.

The results for heavy metal and hydrocarbon analysis are provided in Table A1.3. Only one event had data for both car parks.

Table A1.3 *Water quality results for metals and hydrocarbons (Macdonald and Jefferies, 2001)*

Parameter[1]		Cadmium µg/l	Lead µg/l	Copper µg/l	Chromium µg/l	Nickel µg/l	Zinc µg/l	Hydrocarbons mg/l
Average[2]	Impermeable	0.3	2.76	5.05	0.68	4.64	29.4	1.07
	Pervious	1.91	9.8	10.9	5.73	3.78	42	0.4
Range of EMCs	Impermeable	0.3	2.76	5.05	0.68	4.64	29.4	1.07
	Pervious	0.12–5.33	0.93–24.3	3.76–23.07	3.85–8.73	0.95–8.69	17–67	0.12–1.21
EMC reducn/increase (-/+)[3, 4]		-4%	-66%	−25.5%	580%	-63%	-42%	-69%

Notes

1. Three events metals, four for hydrocarbons and three spot samples for each.
2. Calculated from EMC for each event.
3. Calculated from reduction/increase for individual events, ie not the difference between the average.
4. From only one event.

The results demonstrate a reduction in the event mean concentrations of heavy metals and hydrocarbons in the runoff from the pervious surface, except for chromium, which increased. The concentration of heavy metals from the pervious surface are all below the levels required for drinking water (Water Supply (Water Quality) Regulations 2000).

Case Study No 3

Location	Royal Bank of Scotland, Edinburgh, car park
Lessons to be learned from this case study	Pervious surfaces can treat pollution washed off urban surfaces by rainfall to reduce pollutant levels and they can significantly reduce both peak flows and the total volume of outflow.
Date of construction	1998, 20 months old when monitoring undertaken
Design philosophy	The car park is an extension to conventional impermeable car park adjacent to the Royal Bank of Scotland headquarters in Edinburgh. The pervious surface car park is 0.62 ha in area. The construction comprises a permeable concrete block surface installed to the manufacturer's specification, which typically comprises a 80 mm block over a 50 mm bedding layer of 5 mm single-size gravel over a geotextile over 350 mm of open sub-base to the following grading: **Sieve size** **Percentage by mass passing** 100 mm 100 80 mm 80–100 60 mm 60–80 40 mm 30–50 20 mm 0–20 10 mm 0–5 Note some of these are not standard sieve sizes and should not be used to specify aggregate. The system is tanked with an impermeable geomembrane and the outflow is via a series of perforated pipes (eight) to a 450 mm-diameter storm sewer. A plan of the drainage layout is provided on Figure A1.6.
Maintenance	Details of the maintenance regime are not available.
General comments	The information in this case study was obtained from Schluter and Jefferies, 2001.

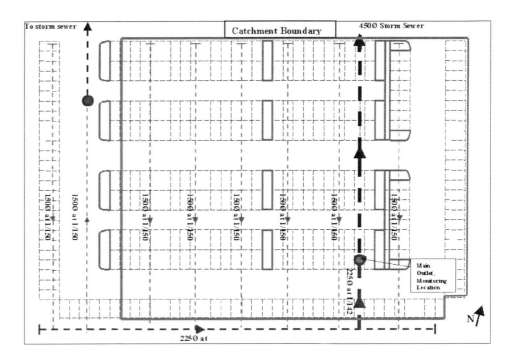

Figure A1.6 *Drainage layout (Schluter and Jefferies, 2001)*

Hydraulic performance

Monitoring

The system was monitored for hydraulic performance from 16 February to 10 August 2000 in a monitoring manhole receiving runoff from six of the eight perforated outlet pipes.

Results

The results from the hydraulic monitoring demonstrate the effectiveness of pervious pavements in reducing the peak outflow rate and total volume of runoff. A typical hydrograph from the site is provided in Figure A1.7.

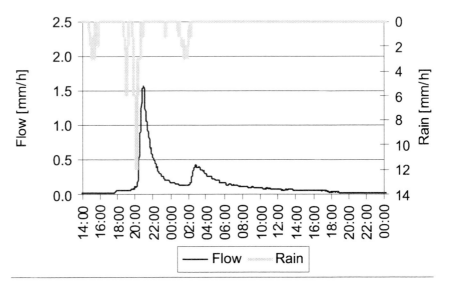

Figure A1.7 *Typical hydrograph from pervious surface (Schluter and Jefferies, 2001)*

The lag time between the centre of gravity of the rainfall to the peak outflow varied between 42 minutes and 143 minutes, with the shorter times relating to medium rainfall events. This compares to typical values for impermeable surfaces of around five minutes.

A comparison of rainfall with outflow is provided in Figure A1.8.

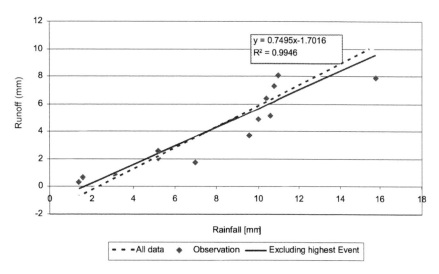

Figure A1.8 *Comparison of rainfall with outflow (Schluter and Jefferies, 2001)*

The percentage outflow varied between 14.2 per cent to 79.5 per cent, with an average of 46.5 per cent. The precise percentage was observed to depend on the duration of the rainfall event, total rainfall and antecedent precipitation. The difference was attributed to evaporation or being retained within the pervious pavement construction.

Structural performance

There is no quantitative information on the structural performance of this car park. However, anecdotal evidence indicates it has not suffered any failure to date.

Water quality performance

Water quality monitoring was carried out for two months at the end of the hydraulic monitoring period. Seven flow events were monitored and quality data was obtained from four events. In addition, spot samples were taken on every visit regardless of flow.

The testing undertaken is summarised below:

06 Jun 00 to 07 Jun 00	General quality screening tests
08 Jul 00 to 09 Jul 00	General quality screening tests
31 Jul 00 to 01 Aug 00	Hydrocarbons
09 Aug 00 to 10 Aug 00	General quality screening tests, hydrocarbons

A summary of the water analyses are provided in Tables A1.4, A1.5 and A1.6. In general, all the parameters are low when compared to the levels found in runoff from conventional roads (Luker and Montague, 1994) and are below the levels required for drinking water (Water Supply (Water Quality) Regulations 2000).

The pH results are permanently slightly alkaline and show very little variation. Total suspended solids were generally higher during events than from spot samples, and this may be due to the flush effect during increased flows. Ammoniacal nitrogen and BOD values were generally very low. One extreme nitrogen result was obtained during the peak of one event with a maximum concentration of 0.57 mg/l, whereas other results indicate nitrogen concentrations of 0.02 mg/l. Total chloride and conductivity were also low. When there is an increase in flows out of the system, it seems to cause dilution of the pollutants with reduced concentrations occurring.

Table A1.4 *Water quality results for general quality parameters*

Event date		06/06/00 to 07/06/00			09/07/00 to 09/07/00			09/08/00 to 10/08/00			Spot sampling		
		min	max	mean	min	max	mean	min	max	mean	min	max	mean
pH	[-]	7.8	8.2	8	8.1	8.2	8.1	7.9	8.6	8.1	7.4	8.2	8
Conductivity	[uS/cm]	281	615	447	550	581	553	365	929	541	358	730	544
TSS	[mg/l]	6.6	39.9	23.2	3.7	8.2	6	0	68	11.6	1	16.1	8.2
BOD	[mg/l]	1.6	3	1.96	3	10	4.38	2	2	2	0.7	3	2
NH4N	[mg/l]	0.03	0.57	0.11	0.04	0.06	0.05	0.02	0.2	0.1	<0.02	0.04	0.03
Oxidised nitrogen	[mg/l]	1.05	2.04	1.58	2.75	3.02	2.92	1.23	1.23	1.48	1.15	2.15	1.53
Ortho-phosphate	[mg/l]	0.05	0.23	0.14	0.04	0.11	0.07	0.02	0.24	0.06	0.01	0.04	0.03
Chloride	[mg/l]	13.5	32.7	23.8	20.2	24.3	21.8	6.4	42.6	20	8.5	34.9	24.8
No of samples	[-]	22			5			42			9		

Table A1.5 *Water quality results for hydrocarbons*

Start and end time of sampling		31/07/00 to 01/08/00			09/08/00 to 10/08/00			Spot sampling		
		min	max	mean	min	max	mean	min	max	mean
Hydrocarbons	[mg/l]	0.375	3.35	1.97	0.1*	0.1*	0.1*	0.1*	0.27	0.1
Number of samples taken	[mg/l]	12			12			6		

* values below detection limit

Hydrocarbon results are generally below the limit of detection except for the event on 31 July 2000. This recorded hydrocarbon concentrations between 0.375 mg/l and 3.35 mg/l, which are slightly elevated. There is insufficient data to determine the cause of this. The results show that the pervious surface is reducing the amount of hydrocarbons in the runoff when compared with the levels found in runoff from conventional roads (Luker and Montague, 1994).

Only spot samples were analysed for heavy metals. Nine samples were taken and the results are summarised below. All the results are below the levels required for drinking water as specified in the Water Supply (Water Quality) Regulations 2000.

Table A1.6 *Results from heavy metals analysis*

Pollutant	Cadmium µg/l	Lead µg/l	Chromium mg/l	Copper µg/l	Nickel µg/l	Zinc µg/l
minimum	<0.066	0.9	<1.7	1.7	0.81	9
maximum	<0.066	2.6	4.5	9.5	4	32
mean	<0.068	1.8	2.2	5.2	1.7	22.2
Number of samples	9					

CASE STUDY NO 4

Location	Tesco, Wokingham, car park

Lessons to be learned from this case study	Porous asphalt should use nominal 20 mm aggregate as defined in the *Specification for Highway Works* to minimise the risk of pores being blocked. Porous asphalt that has become blocked can be improved by installing channels and gullies to direct water to the underlying sub-base, thereby retaining some, though not all, of the benefits of the pervious surface.

Date of construction	Completed early 1998

Design philosophy	Pervious pavement is used in the car parking bays, comprising porous asphalt surfacing over an open sub-base.
	The sub-base has internal dams to maximise attenuation. Porous pipes were used to control the flow of water in the sub-base between dammed areas.
	The sub-base has been seeded with bacteria to help break down hydrocarbon contamination.
	The main access roads used by heavy goods delivery vehicles are constructed using traditional impermeable pavement.

Maintenance	The maintenance regime is not known.

General comments	The information for this case study was provided by the Environment Agency, complemented by inspection of the surface.
	The pervious pavement was cheaper to install than conventional surfacing and drainage (mainly due to the size of the retention tank that would have been required).

Hydraulic performance

Before construction of the scheme, the local brook flooded downstream of the site, and misconnections within the site created capacity problems in the local foul sewage system.

The use of pervious pavements (together with other SUDS methods) reduced the peak flows and volumes in the brook and reduced the local flooding from both the brook and foul sewer (see Figure A1.9).

The groundwater table is high, so infiltration was not possible and the system was constructed with a sealed membrane below the base.

Anecdotal evidence indicates that ponding has occurred regularly since installation. In early 2002 gullies and channels were installed to allow water in these ponding areas to pass into the underlying sub-base construction. Inspection of the surface reveals that the porous asphalt has a relatively small-size aggregate (10 mm, based on visual inspection), which is smaller than the aggregate size adopted in the *Specification for*

Highway Works (20 mm) and could be more susceptible to blocking. Anecdotal evidence suggests that it is clogged in the more heavily trafficked areas, although no quantitative data is available to confirm this.

(Note: care should be taken to prevent silt entering the sub-base if this form of remedial works are adopted).

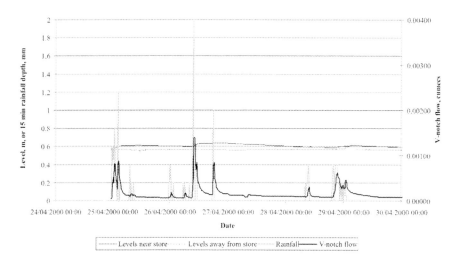

Figure A1.9 *Typical hydrograph from pervious surface and effects on stream*

Structural performance

There is no quantitative structural data for the site. However there are no apparent structural problems with the pavement.

Water quality performance

The water from the pervious pavement is discharged to a reed bed for treatment prior to discharge to the local watercourse. The sub-base has been seeded with bacteria to help break down hydrocarbon contamination. The Environment Agency monitor water quality in the system but the data has not been made available.

CASE STUDY NO 5

Location	Wheatley Motorway Service Area (MSA), M40, Oxford, car park
Lessons to be learned from this case study	Pervious surfaces can be integrated within a wider SUDS system and can work as infiltration devices. Specification of the sub-base material is important. Infiltration rates deteriorate over time, which should be allowed for in design. Regular cleaning is required and dirt and debris should be prevented from being compacted into the pervious surface, particularly next to planted areas.
Date of construction	Completed 1998

Design philosophy	The pervious pavement was one element of a much larger SUDS scheme, promoted by the landscape architect and the Environment Agency. The rainfall is stored in the pavement sub-base before being discharged to a series of swales, interceptor ponds and a reed bed wetland.

The pervious pavement was constructed with a sealed base with a geomembrane liner due to concerns about groundwater pollution from natural arsenic in the soils below the site.

The car park construction comprises 80 mm concrete blocks over 50 mm-thick 5 mm single-size aggregate. This lies on a geotextile over the 350 mm-thick sub base to the following specification:

Sieve size	Percentage by mass passing
100 mm	100
80 mm	80–100
60 mm	60–80
40 mm	30–50
20 mm	0–20
10 mm	0–5

Note some of these are not standard sieve sizes and should not be used to specify aggregate.

The base is sealed with an impermeable geomembrane and outflow is via a 225 mm-diameter pipe from the sub-base at the low end of the car park (see Figure A1.10).

The pervious area is 6250 m^2 and this drains a total area of 12 400 m^2. |
| **Maintenance** | The specified maintenance is to suction-sweep the surface twice a year. |
| **General comments** | The information in this case study was obtained from CIRIA, 2001a; Abbott *et al*, 2000 and personal communication with C Abbott. |

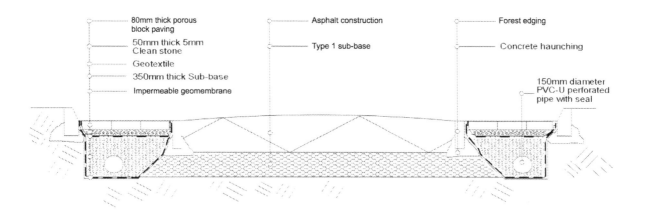

Figure A1.10 *Cross-section through pavement construction showing pervious and impermeable construction*

Hydraulic performance

Monitoring was undertaken at a chamber 150 m downstream from the car park between December 1998 and January 2000. A typical hydrograph is shown in Figure A1.11. Infiltration tests were also undertaken on the pervious surface using an infiltrometer developed by the Transport Research Laboratory (TRL) in May 1999 and in February 2000.

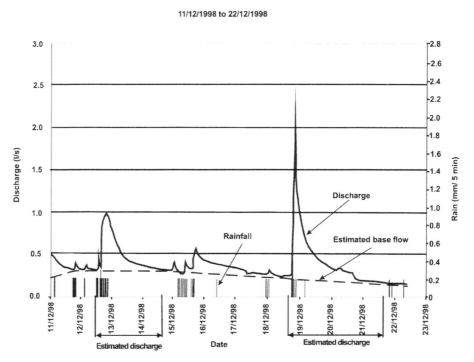

Figure A1.11 *Typical hydrograph from outfall of pervious pavement at Wheatley MSA*

The peak discharge rates varied from 0.9 l/s to 13.5 l/s and the peak outflow corresponding to a rainfall intensity of 12 mm/h was only 0.37 mm/h, demonstrating the effective attenuation of the stormwater. The average peak discharge compared with peak rainfall varied from 1 per cent to 33 per cent.

The time delay (similar to lag time) between rain falling on the surface and a rise in flow in the outlet varied from five minutes to more than two hours. The delay between the storm peak and the peak discharge ranged from five minutes to more than nine hours. On average the discharge lasted 14 times longer than the rainfall, again demonstrating effective attenuation.

The observations made suggest that an average of 67 per cent of rainfall percolates through the system. The remaining volume is removed by mechanisms such as evaporation, loss through defects in the geomembrane and lateral overflow from the system.

The TRL infiltrometer was used to measure the performance of both the concrete blocks and the gaps between them. The results gave a wide scatter.

Infiltration through the bricks initially varied between 250 mm/h and 14 000 mm/h. Ten months later infiltration through the blocks was not possible. This was due to the accumulation of silt, moss and oil on the surface, which had not been removed. Regular maintenance would have avoided this. It is, however, affecting only the main infiltration pathway between the bricks in very localised areas, adjacent to planting, where small areas of localised ponding occur. It does not adversely affect overall operation of the system.

Infiltration through the gaps varied from 11 000 mm/h to 229 500 mm/h. After 10 months the results were between 10 300 mm/h and 388 000 mm/h suggesting no significant decrease in infiltration rate. The infiltration rate nevertheless remains much greater than required.

Structural performance

There is no quantitative data on the structural performance of the car park. Abbott *et al* (2000) noted that some areas of the car park suffered from subsidence and damage to the surface. The sub-base came from a source comprising oolitic limestone, and a large volume of fines that appeared to be derived from this were noted in the outflow. The exact source is not known in this case, but this material is typically a weak rock and is likely to degrade under the action of repeated wetting and drying and may crush under construction traffic loads, which could have caused the problems. This would be avoided by correct specification of a hard and durable sub-base.

Water quality performance

There is no data on water quality.

CASE STUDY NO 6

Location	Powells Creek, Concord, New South Wales, Australia
Lessons to be learned from this case study	Pervious surfaces can significantly improve runoff quality. The use of bio-engineered filter layers can be beneficial. Careful design of the bio-engineered soils and pervious surface is required to avoid the vegetation dying, and good maintenance is needed to avoid blockage of the surface. Pervious systems can be retrofitted to existing developments, as in this scheme.
Date of construction	December 1998
Design philosophy	This is an example of an infiltration strip or trench incorporating a pervious surface. Also it demonstrates the potential for pervious surfaces to improve water quality. The pervious strip is located along the edges of residential roads. The strips of pervious pavement are about 500 mm wide and infiltrate the runoff from the impermeable road pavement. The total area draining to the system is approximately 1330 m^2. The objective of the scheme is to improve water quality in the receiving waters, and reduce runoff volumes to a local stream. The Concord project is a stormwater purification and recycling system designed to treat and restore stormwater runoff close to drinking water quality. Prior to the project, the runoff from the site was collected by a typical curb and gutter inlet. Untreated runoff from this was directed into storm sewers. The system was designed to replace the traditional stormwater systems and to treat stormwater runoff from the streets and their surrounds. The water was then to be infiltrated to the ground, reused for irrigation, or alternatively, to be safely discharged into Powells Creek.

Design philosophy	It comprises a permeable plastic grid-paving block, with turf growing in grid cells, located along the edge of each side of the streets. The runoff infiltrates through the paving blocks. The blocks are bedded on a filter layer comprising a proprietary sand filter. The filter sand has a high adsorption capacity (based on its cationic exchange efficiency of 160 meq compared to 2 meq for normal sand). The runoff then flows into subsurface vertical cells with dimensions of 900 mm × 400 mm and wrapped in a 2 mm woven filtration geotextile (see Figure A1.12) The soils below the site consist of topsoil and fill, overlaying silty clays and weathered shale. Natural silty clays are present at depths of 2.1–3.0 m with pockets of manmade fill. Soil permeability tests were performed *in situ* using falling head tests and indicated a clay with permeability of 10^{-9} m/sec. With such a low permeability, infiltration is likely to be minimal.

Maintenance	Details of the maintenance undertaken are not available.

General comments	The information in this case study was provided by Nick Cooper of Alderburgh Limited with additional information from a report on the system for Concord Council (Australian Water Technologies, 1999) and a site visit undertaken by C Pratt. Aesthetically, the condition of the grass on the parking aisle areas was a concern, because much of the turf died soon after installation resulting in the exposure of the cell grid beneath. During the winter months silts and decayed leaf litter clogged grid cells, reducing the infiltration rates in the system (based on visual observations). This should have been avoided with adequate maintenance.

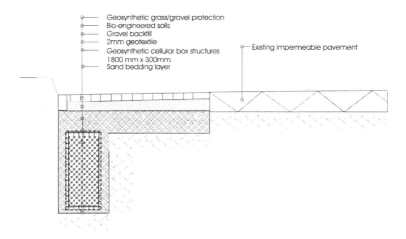

Figure A1.12 *Construction details of pervious pavement along edges of road*

Hydraulic performance

The scheme is reported to have reduced overall runoff into Powell Creek by 75 per cent, although there is no quantitative data available.

Structural performance

There is no data on the structural performance of the system under traffic loads.

Water quality performance

Independent testing of the water quality of the receiving stream was undertaken by Australian Water Technologies on behalf of Concord Council. The monitoring was undertaken at locations upstream and downstream of the system during 10 storm events over a four-month period in 1999.

The upstream sampling point collected water flowing from the impermeable catchment on to the pervious surface. The water was diverted into a collection system that automatically sampled the runoff when a storm event occurred. The downstream samples were taken manually from a stormwater detention tank to which the system was connected.

The results show a reduction in the level of heavy metals, suspended solids, PAH, phosphorous and nitrogen (see table below). Faecal coliforms were only tested in the downstream tank and were below the levels required for use as irrigation water in Australia (maximum 400 cfu/100 mL and minimum of zero cfu/100 mL). There was a significant increase in conductivity, which was not explained.

Table A1.7 *Reduction in pollutants between upstream and downstream locations*

	pH	Conductivity mS/m	Turbidity ntu	Copper mg/l	Lead mg/l	Zinc mg/l	Phosphorous mg/l	Nitrogen mg/l	PAH mg/l	Suspended solids mg/l
Upstream										
Minimum	6.98	10.6	139	29	36	93	0.005	0.82	< 0.1	9
Maximum	8.91	46.6	1302	173	340	1010	0.73	4.27	8.8	786
Mean	7.79	24.3	448.7	75	133	276	0.264	1.97	3.7	291
Downstream										
Minimum	7.5	35	3.9	3	< 1.0	< 5.0	0.011	0.94	< 0.1	4
Maximum	10.32	109.3	184	7	2	10	0.305	2.14	1.1	189
Mean	9.08	61.9	41.8	5	1	6	0.057	1.46	0.6	50
Percentage change from upstream to downstream means	171	350	-90.7	-93.6	-99.4	-97.9	-78.6	-25.9	-83.8	-82.8

Notes

1. Increase in pH was reported to be due to the effects of fresh concrete on stored water in the detention tank.

A2   Further research

The design of pervious surfaces seems to be conservative, but as research is carried out the design process will be refined. There are several perceived barriers to the widespread adoption of pervious pavements. Research should be focused on collecting data that can be used to overcome these perceptions, particularly performance data from constructed systems. As a result of the CIRIA research project, some specific research needs have been identified that will enhance the design process.

It is clear that widespread monitoring of the water quality aspects of pervious pavement performance should be a priority, to confirm laboratory evidence of quality improvements. The hydraulic performance of such pavements is important, and while the possible blockage and ponding on the surface is of concern, these aspects should be incorporated in the water quality investigations. Some structural aspects also need further research. The research needs are summarised below.

Water quality and hydraulic performance

There is a shortage of data from a range of types of operational pervious surfaces. Good data is forthcoming from two sites in Edinburgh and some short-term data from a site in Australia, but little else is available (Macdonald and Jefferies, 2001; Schluter and Jefferies, 2001, Australian Water Technologies, 1999). An expansion in field studies may provide information on the impact of land use (both on the pervious surface and nearby), seasonal changes in pollutant supply and throughput, operational maintenance needs, and overall quantity and quality performance.

Specific research is needed on geotextiles in the construction:

- should there be one at the high level, below the surfacing materials, or is it better to accumulate any sludge at the base of the pavement?
- if there is a geotextile, or more than one at different locations, what type and characteristics should be chosen to enhance pollutant-trapping efficiency?

It is important to establish whether bio-remediation can be naturally established within all such pervious structures, what pollutants can be treated and how can the process be optimised.

The long-term availability of aggregates is in doubt, as their cost is rising steadily. The question is whether these materials can be exchanged for sustainable ones and still achieve present performance in water quantity and quality terms, or even enhance it. Several plastic box and modular drainage systems are commercially available, but their value for improving water quality is unknown.

The most important issue, and the most difficult to resolve, is the impact of the passage of dissolved pollutants through pervious constructions where the waters percolate the soil beneath by way of disposal. Laboratory models are unsatisfactory, except in the development of pre-treatment processes. Field studies are expensive, and care must be exercised that measurement techniques do not distort the percolation and chemical/biological processes at work in the soil horizons.

Research is also required to confirm:

- the accurate length of operating life
- effects of different maintenance regimes
- groundwater impacts from recently constructed surfaces.

Nevertheless, there are still advantages to greater use of pervious surfaces and structures in both water quantity and quality terms, particularly when compared to traditional sewerage systems.

Structural performance

To allow the routine use of pervious pavements in locations with heavy axle loads, more test demonstration sites are required, which should be monitored and instrumentation installed. In particular, the following effects need to be more clearly understood:

- performance of saturated subgrades
- aggregate grading and performance under load
- performance of geosynthetic structures
- development of a standard set of specifications for materials and installation
- effects of polluted runoff: for example, petrol spills on open-graded asphalt or geosynthetic structures.

A3   Design information checklist

Description	Details for the particular project	Consultees and sources of information
Existing site parameters		
Physical		
Topography		Site survey or inspection
Area of catchment		Site survey
Soil type		Site investigation
Infiltration potential of soil		Site investigation
Structural properties of soil – CBR, stiffness		Site investigation and laboratory testing
Former land use		Local authority, Ordnance Survey maps, local library
Hydraulic		
Hydrology of catchment		Site inspection and observations
Flood risk		Environment Agency/SEPA/DoE in Northern Ireland/local authority
Rainfall data		Meteorological Office or Wallingford Procedure
Discharge design criteria – quantity		Environment Agency/SEPA/DoE in Northern Ireland or water service company
Discharge design criteria – quality		Environment Agency/SEPA/DoE in Northern Ireland or water service company
Frequency of ponding on surface that is acceptable		Owner/operator
Storage capacity and permeability of materials		Laboratory testing and test sections or manufacturer's specifications
Environmental		
Contamination of ground below site		Local authority, Ordnance Survey maps, local library and site investigation
Details of receiving water/watercourse/aquifer		Environment Agency/SEPA/DoE in Northern Ireland or water service company
Environmental sensitivity of site		Environment Agency/SEPA/DoE in Northern Ireland/Local Authority, English Nature (Countryside Council in Wales)
Groundwater vulnerability and source protection status		Environment Agency/SEPA/DoE in Northern Ireland
Design-specific parameters		
Site		
Development type and land use		Proposed development plans
Potential area of pervious pavement		Proposed development layout plan
Structural		
Structural properties of materials		Laboratory testing and test sections or manufacturer's specifications
Construction and design traffic loads		Proposed development plans
Health and safety		All affected parties

A4   Maintenance

The issue of long-term maintenance should be reviewed regularly, as performance data becomes available from long-term monitoring of installed systems. The maintenance provisions to ensure adequate long-term performance of the pavement, will vary according to the type of application, site location and type of pavement system used (Section 3.3).

As with any pavement structure, a routine and long-term maintenance programme needs to be developed to suit the requirements of each installation. There is considerable evidence worldwide to refute the perception of pervious pavements requiring far higher levels of maintenance than conventional construction.

If permeable pavements are used to drain adjacent roofs or impermeable areas, care should be taken to avoid sediment entering the pavement and blocking the pores. This can be achieved by passing runoff from adjacent areas through screens (on roof downpipes), vortex filters or gully silt traps (on paved surfaces). Water from these sources can be piped into the sub-base of the pavement, avoiding any risk of ponding on the surface.

Maintenance of permeable pavements falls into two categories:

- regular maintenance
- remedial maintenance.

The owner or operator of a site where pervious surfaces have been installed should be provided with a clear schedule of inspection and maintenance requirements (Section 3.3). A list of typical requirements is provided in Table A4.1.

Table A4.1   *Maintenance requirements for pervious surfaces (Fenner, 2001)*

Maintenance requirement	Description	Surface or sub-surface	Regular	Remedial
Inspection	Inspect catchpits at outlets once a year (if appropriate)	Surface	Yes	
Surface cleaning	To minimise clogging, clean dirt and other matter from the surface at least twice a year by vacuum-sweeping, early spring (after winter) and autumn (after leaf fall)	Surface	Yes	
Managing vegetation	Weed control between blocks (use non-toxic biodegradable weedkillers)	Surface	Yes	
Re-establish infiltration capacity	For block surfaces, lift surface and replace gravel bedding and geotextile as necessary.	Sub-surface		Yes
	For continuous concrete permeable surfaces, replace gravel infill.			Yes
	For continuous porous surfaces, replace surface.			Yes
	(All likely to be after a period of about 15–20 years.)			
Screen runoff from adjacent areas	Pass through screens on downpipes, filters or use gully silt traps	Surface	Yes	
Good housekeeping	Minimise use of salt or grit for de-icing, keep landscaped areas well maintained and prevent soil being washed on to pavement.	Surface	Yes	

Appendix 4

Regular maintenance

The surface should be inspected regularly for signs of both structural failure (cracking or displacement between blocks) and hydraulic failure (surface ponding after storms).

Vacuum-sweeping should be carried out at least twice a year: at the beginning of spring, when general landscape tidying of winter damage is undertaken, and in the autumn, after leaf fall. Depending on the site use, sweeping may be required more often (which may occur anyway for good housekeeping reasons).

Between sweeping cycles, general good housekeeping should minimise the impact of nearby activities. Weeds should not present a problem because the sub-base will be too dry to support any plant growth. If weed control is necessary, manual control or non-toxic and biodegradable weedkillers should be used.

People working on or using permeable pavements should be made aware of their general environmental responsibility. Displaying a clear public notice to this effect will encourage responsible behaviour and increase the awareness of SUDS.

If the surface is chosen correctly, its free-draining surface, coupled with the lag in temperature change within the pavement, should reduce the need for de-icing salts or gritting. Use of salt or grit should be avoided, as these impair the flow of water through the surface and will unnecessarily contribute to pollution. A risk assessment should be undertaken before considering a policy of no salting or gritting.

Any outflow pipes should be inspected regularly and any blockages removed.

Remedial maintenance

Where areas of the pavement show decreased infiltration, or after a major accidental spillage, they might require remedial maintenance. Initially, the porous surface or the inlets to the permeable pavement sub-base should be cleaned or individual areas treated.

If this process fails to produce satisfactory results it will be necessary to lift the surfacing materials, possibly remove and replace the bedding gravel, and reinstate the surface. For permeable pavements with large voids (such as gravel surfaces or open-cell concrete), this process is not particularly time-consuming, onerous or expensive, and surface materials may be reused several times. However, when porous concrete or porous asphalt becomes blocked, the surface will normally need to be replaced with new porous blocks or porous asphalt.

A5   Whole-life costing

The commercial viability of pervious pavement construction needs careful consideration at the concept planning stage of a project. Cost appraisals need to look not only at the initial capital cost but at the "whole-life costs". Recent cost comparisons have proven the cost-effectiveness of utilising source control techniques in place of traditional positive drainage systems. The evaluation of the relative whole-life costing of construction options must be based upon actual data, particularly taking into consideration the economic and environmental benefits of each option.

The following needs to be considered in whole-life costing models for pervious pavements:

- absence of conventional kerbs and gullies
- much reduced need for pipes, manholes etc and absence of deep trench excavations
- requirements to enlarge receiving sewer system for conventional drainage
- absence of storage tanks, leading to reduced excavations and construction costs
- smaller charges to water companies where rainwater is not be conveyed to sewers
- less need for wayleaves and easements to construct sewer outfalls
- comparison of maintenance requirements between conventional drainage and pervious surfaces, including frequency of both routine and non-routine (Section 3.3)
- excavation to achieve the required levels on both the pervious or conventional pavement
- possible simpler construction with pervious surfaces
- construction programme
- life-span of whole system
- replacement costs
- cost of providing additional treatment at outlets, should this prove to be necessary (Section 5.4.5)
- environmental improvements (although these are difficult to quantify in financial terms).

Where adoption is proposed, a financial appraisal should be carried out that will identify the costs appropriate to both the developer (capital costs) and the adopting authority (maintenance and replacement costs).

Detailed cost data is not provided because of the wide range of pervious pavement systems, each of which will be site-specific. Unit costs can be obtained using manufacturer's prices and published unit rate data.

A method of undertaking a cost comparison is described in CIRIA Report 156 (Bettess, 1996).

A6 Review of water quality data from literature

Laboratory results of the runoff, retention and through-flow of pollutants from four different surfaces were reported in 1981 by Day *et al*. The four surfaces were a traditional concrete paved surface, two large-element permeable-block surfaces and a continuous-laid permeable concrete surface. Various artificial rainfalls containing pollutants were applied to the test surfaces and the water volume and quality of the surface runoff and percolated waters were measured. Each of the permeable surfaces were constructed in a box with a drainage layer at its base, over which was some 300 mm of a typical subsoil. Each permeable surface was laid on the manufacturer's recommended substructure on top of the soil. The substructure was typically 50 mm sand over 150 mm gravel. Topsoil was used to fill the voids in the pavement surface. The mean percentage runoffs for the surfaces are given in Table A6.1

Table A6.1   *Mean percentage runoff from pavement surface*

Type of surface	Percentage runoff
Large elemental, permeable block	0
Continuous-laid permeable	0.5
Concrete paved	78

The pollutant concentrations in runoff that did occur from the continuous-laid permeable surface were greater than the corresponding ones for the concrete slab, except for organic phosphorus and heavy metals. However, the pollutant load being discharged in the surface waters was much less for the permeable surface than for the concrete slab, because of the significant differences in the runoff volumes. In the case of lead in the runoff, the mass from the concrete slab was found to be 350 times greater than from the permeable surface.

Samples of the percolating waters were obtained from near the top of the subsoil layer below the permeable surfaces. This showed a significant reduction in some contaminants when compared to the conventional pavement. Significant removal of pollutants was also reported at Concords Road in Australia (Australian Water Technologies, 1999). The results of both studies are summarised in Table A6.2.

Table A6.2 *Pollutant removal by pervious surfaces*

Pollutant	Percentage removal	
	Day et al, 1981	**Australian Water Technologies, 2000**
Total, ortho and organic phosphate phosphorus	> 75 per cent (increased retention with depth and the presence of clay-sized particles)	78.60 per cent
Organic nitrogen	70–80 per cent	25.90 per cent
Ammonia	26–78 per cent	—
Total organic carbon (TOC)	5–76 per cent	—
Turbidity	—	90.70 per cent
Suspended solids	—	82.80 per cent
Copper	—	93.60 per cent
Lead	94–98 per cent	99.40 per cent
Zinc	90–97 per cent	97.90 per cent
Chromium	45–94 per cent	—
PAH	—	83.8 per cent

A similar laboratory study was reported by Hogland (1990), which looked at pollutant transport and retention with porous asphalt. This Swedish construction consisted of a 40 mm surfacing layer with 15–24 per cent voids overlaying two layers of free-draining aggregate. The upper layer of aggregate, some 40 mm deep, formed of 4–25 mm aggregates and acted as a levelling course, below which was a 300–700 mm sub-base layer of 30–70 mm aggregates. In practice, the construction is separated by a geotextile layer from the sub-grade, which is typically boulder clay and effectively impermeable.

Artificial rainfall using highway runoff was applied to 12 test samples of the porous pavement over various periods to simulate the pollutant retention of the pavement in service for between 18 months and 30 years. The laboratory constructions had a 500 mm sub-base layer over 500 mm boulder clay. After the simulated timespan for an experiment the pavement was dismantled and the pollutant concentrations at various depths within the construction was determined. The concentrations varied with depth, with the highest for all pollutants analysed being at the geotextile on the base of the construction, except for chloride and nitrite/nitrate, the latter being highest in the porous asphalt.

Sediment accumulated on top of the geotextile and much of it was organic in nature. This trapped organic material adsorbs heavy metals and accounts for their elevated levels at that depth in the pavement. Nitrite/nitrate and ammonia concentrations were also higher at the geotextile than within the sub-base generally. In the soil below the geotextile, sulphur showed an 11-fold increase on the initial value in the soil; ammonia, zinc and total phosphorus up to a four-fold increase; otherwise other pollutants displayed lower values. Analysis conducted on samples obtained from a operational pavement during its reconstruction showed total phosphorus, total solids, copper and cadmium at their highest concentration in the boulder clay below the geotextile, whereas most other pollutants were at the highest levels on the geotextile. The lowest concentrations were at the mid-depth in the sub-base aggregate, suggesting that pollutants were either trapped in the porous surface or transported to the base of the construction, where they might be retained or discharged from the sub-base drain, located just above the geotextile. Analyses of drain effluent showed that concentrations of suspended solids, total solids, chromium and aluminium were markedly lower than typical discharges from impermeable surfaces and that concentrations of copper, zinc and lead were reduced, but less so. An increase in concentration was found for nitrite/nitrate, ammonia and chlorides, thought in part due to the use of de-icing agents.

Also in the late 1980s, water quality sampling was undertaken on a small-element, permeable-block-surfaced car park at Nottingham Trent University (Pratt, 1995) during its first three years of operation. The concrete surfacing blocks were laid on a 50 mm-thick layer of 5–10 mm gravel, which was spread over a geotextile layer (used to prevent the gravel from falling into the voids in the free-drainage aggregate sub-base below). The sub-base layer varied in thickness from 300 mm to 400 mm across the width of the pavement, causing the internal waters to flow to a drainpipe, which passed through the geomembrane wall to the monitoring point. Four aggregate types were used for the sub-base, each contained within a separately drained, impermeable geomembrane, so that all throughflow could be monitored separately at the outfall of the drain from each of the geomembrane-lined compartments. The aggregate types were as follows.

1. Gravel 6–20 mm.
2. Blast furnace slag 4–50 mm.
3. Granite 3–40 mm.
4. Carboniferous limestone aggregate 5–50 mm.

Each of the four sub-base aggregates produced a different range of values in water quality parameters, although any one parameter was remarkably consistent storm event by event. For instance, the pH and alkalinity of the effluent were lower for the blast furnace slag sub-base discharges as compared with those from the limestone aggregate sub-base. Similarly, hardness and lead were lower in discharges from the limestone aggregate sub-base. The order of the parameter change with aggregate type is listed below.

1. Limestone aggregate.
2. Granite.
3. Gravel.
4. Blast furnace slag.

The direction of change was dependent upon the parameter of interest.

Over about two years of monitoring, the water quality parameters for the four permeable pavement sections showed small, slow variations with time (Pratt, 1995). Blast furnace slag effluent showed a gradual decrease in hardness, whilst both granite and blast furnace slag exhibited slow decreases in conductivity. Variation of suspended solids concentration over the period was limited to a range from near zero to 50 mg/l, after an initial period of sediment flushing due to material brought to the site on the construction materials. This range of suspended solids concentrations is considerably less than is typical for discharges from impermeable surfaces, where fluctuations of 30 mg/l to 300 mg/l occur frequently during storm events, and peak concentrations of several 1000 mg/l are not uncommon. The consistency of concentration of suspended solids in the effluent is in marked contrast to the variability occurring with impermeable surfaces between consecutive events, where antecedent conditions and the storm characteristics determine solids washoff. A limited number of determinations of hydrocarbon concentration in the effluent were attempted, but in all cases they were below the level of detection, suggesting that significant biodegradation was occurring.

Associated with this field study, a laboratory investigation was also made of the locations of pollutant retention within the permeable structure (Schofield, 1994). Urban stormwater was collected from gully pots and pumped on to small-scale, full-size models of the blast furnace slag, granite and limestone aggregate structures, to simulate 10 years' rainfall. In all but one case – that of sediment accumulation for the granite – most of the mass of total sediment, organic material and lead was retained in the 50 mm gravel layer and on the geotextile. None of the aggregate used was pre-washed and in the case of granite, the aggregate was found to have significant initial sediment content. This affected the results by suggesting a more widespread presence of sediment than was actually derived from the stormwater inflow. Overall, the result indicated the significance of the geotextile in limiting the transport of sediment and sediment-associated pollutants deep into the permeable construction.

The observations detailed above show that pollutants are stored within the pervious pavements, but also that pollutants do reach the base of the construction, from where they may infiltrate the soil. The possible transport of such pollutants to groundwater should be considered. Some field data on the movement of heavy metals into the subgrade has been reported for a porous asphalt surfaced residential highway at Rezé, near Nantes in France (Legret et al, 1998).

The porous construction was built in 1988 over a 700 m section of residential road where traffic usage was some 1600 vehicles per day. The subgrade was weathered clay over which was placed a woven geotextile, on which the construction materials were placed. The porous surface comprised the following layers in descending order.

1. A 60 mm layer of 14 mm porous asphalt.

2. Two 100 mm layers of porous bituminous-bound, single-size aggregates.

3. A 300 mm layer of 10–80 mm crushed aggregate.

Stormwater percolating through the construction either infiltrated the subgrade or was intercepted by a perforated sub-base drainage pipe.

In 1996, samples of soil in the 200 mm immediately beneath the construction were analysed for heavy metals and the results compared with the French Agricultural Soil Threshold Standard as summarised in Table A6.3.

Table A6.3 *Pollution migration below soakaways (Legret et al, 1998)*

Pollutant	Soil concentration (mg/kg soil)	French Agricultural Soil Threshold Standard (mg/kg soil)
Cadmium	0.08	2
Copper	11	100
Lead	39	100
Zinc	111	300

Further laboratory-based investigations suggested that lead and, to a lesser degree, copper and zinc concentrations decrease rapidly with depth of soil, being generally nil below 350 mm. Cadmium, on the other hand, is not retained well and can migrate to 700 mm, or beyond, in favourable soil conditions. Legret et al (1998) state that "it is not advisable to install reservoir structures with which the infiltration process is the only means to drain off stormwater, in a zone where the formation level of the structure would be too close to the groundwater table".

Although not directly related to pervious surfaces, a study of the impact of highway runoff on soil and groundwater conducted in Switzerland is informative in the context of stormwater infiltration below such surfaces. Two sites were studied (Mikklesen et al, 1997). At the first one, highway runoff was discharged via a pipe from a kerb inlet gully into a depression on the grass-covered verge. The road carried some 37 000 vehicles per day in 1993 and the drainage had been in service since at least 1959. The second site was located in an industrial city where highway runoff was discharged into

3 m deep soakaways. Traffic density was some 2300 vehicles per day in 1990 and the three soakaways were constructed in 1949 and 1982.

At the first site, high concentrations of heavy metals, a number of polyaromatic hydrocarbons and adsorbed organically bound halogens were found in the upper 500 mm of runoff sludge and soil, but the concentrations decreased rapidly to background levels farther down. At the second site, the runoff sludge was some 200 mm deep and traces of contamination were not found farther than another 200 mm below that level. Similar findings were reported for two soakaways investigated at Brandon, Suffolk (Pratt, 1996). High concentrations of total organic carbon and heavy metals were associated with fine, organic material accumulation in the first 400 mm of sediment in the base of the soakaways. Below 400 mm the pollutant levels appeared to approach those of background levels.

For both the Swiss and UK sites, it was suggested that the formation, and continued presence, of a layer of sludge at the base of the soakaway is important in retaining pollutants by filtration and sorption, resulting in significant build-up of copper, zinc, cadmium, PAHs and halogens in that layer. It was concluded at the Swiss sites that the leaching of heavy metals was limited and that contamination of potable groundwater with metals is of little practical concern within a reasonable time frame. It was also suggested that this conclusion holds for PAHs, which are known to adsorb well in soil. Mikkelsen *et al* (1997) went on to say that soluble components, such as pesticides and de-icing salts, may pass directly through infiltration systems.

Thus, an assessment of possible groundwater contamination with such substances requires other methods of investigation, including mass balances, *in-situ* measurement of concentrations and assessment of the potential degradation of pollutants during passage through infiltration systems.

These findings highlight the possible dangers from dissolved pollutants and from liquids in transport on pervious surfaces with the potential to contaminate groundwater. If the risks to groundwater are considered unacceptable, or the pervious surface is located in a stormwater hotspot (Box 5.4), infiltration should not be allowed and outflow should be by a pipe conveyed to suitable outfall. This would enable effluent quality to be monitored and the system to be shut off in the event of effluent quality problems, such as a major spillage, prior to discharge to an separate infiltration system or another drainage system.

Studies initiated at the car park at Nottingham Trent University in the late 1980s (Scholfield, 1994) were extended through the 1990s in laboratory experiments examining not only the retention but also the degradation of oil within the permeable construction. The previous study had failed to identify hydrocarbons in the effluent from the permeable structure, despite visual evidence of surface contamination through car sump leakage. The fate of these pollutants warranted further study.

A full-size model of the permeable construction at the Nottingham car park, 610 mm by 610 mm surface area, was built and supplied with artificial rainfall and clean mineral oil regularly each week over an extended period of four years (Pratt, 1999). The research aimed to determine whether the retained oil could be degraded through microbial action, ie could the free-draining structure act as an aerobic digestor. Accordingly, the model was seeded with a commercially available bacterial inoculum and nutrients. Both liquid and granular forms of nutrient were tried, with the latter giving better degradation results, and the levels of nutrient concentrations in the effluent were low.

The model drained through its base, and samples of effluent were analysed for oil and grease, total nitrogen, phosphate phosphorus and potassium. Results reported in 1999 showed that 98.7 per cent of the applied oil was retained/degraded over the period and that, with an input oil concentration of 1800 mg/l, the effluent oil concentration was only in the range 3.8–39.5 mg/l. The fact that degradation was occurring was established by the measurement of elevated levels of carbon dioxide within the pavement and by the use of a second model, which allowed a mass balance for oil to be constructed. The measured oil degradation rate using granular nutrients was equivalent to 356 g/m^2/year and it was estimated that the mean residence time of the oil in the structure was some seven months.

Examination of the component materials within the permeable structure showed that around 60–90 per cent oil was retained on the geotextile, from where it would be slowly released and degraded. The long-term capacity of the structure to retain oils was investigated by immersing samples of the component materials in an oil bath for 15 minutes and then allowing them to drain for 25 days before weighing.

These tests showed that some 9.5 kg oil could be retained in total per square metre surface area. The percentage retained in each layer is shown in Table A6.4.

Table A6.4 *Retention of pollutant within pavement structure (Pratt, 1999)*

Pavement layer	Oil retention capacity of material (g oil /kg material)	Percentage retention within as built structure
Concrete blocks	17	12%
Gravel bedding layer	36	29%
Geotextile	3190	5%
Granite sub-base	7	54%

Using these results, a hypothetical car park design was assessed for its potential to become saturated with oil (Pratt, 1999). The car park was assumed to have 4690 m^2 impermeable surface area, all of which drained to a permeable surface side strip of 310 m^2. Using the same oil input concentration of 1800 mg/l – which is 100 times the concentrations the literature identifies as likely in highway runoff – the permeable strip was estimated to have a 44-year life before saturation. If the total area of the car park was constructed as a permeable structure, the time to saturation was estimated to exceed 100 years, not allowing for degradation of the oil that will occur in the long term. This appears to suggest that oil saturation is not a major problem where supply is evenly spread over time at this high, but limited, level. A major spill would necessitate the closure of the outlet drain, assuming an impermeable underseal, and significant remedial works.

Studies of the microbial communities that became established in model permeable pavements of the Nottingham type have shown that it is unnecessary to inoculate the surface in order to establish microbial populations. It has been observed that indigenous communities exist on construction materials, when delivered, and that wind-blown deposits provide another effective inoculation route. The nutrients concentrations in the flow from the laboratory model pavement were of acceptable levels as shown in Table A6.5.

Table A6.5 *Nutrient concentrations in flow from laboratory pavement (Bond et al, 1999)*

Nutrient	Concentration in flow (mg/l)
total nitrogen	2.33
nitrite/nitrate nitrogen	1.16
phosphate phosphorus	1.1
potassium	3.13

Nevertheless, it is undesirable to add nutrients to the environment unnecessarily. While unproven, it is thought likely that nutrients occurring in the environment near pervious surfaces, such as in grass cuttings, leaves and animal droppings, may well provide the required stimulus for indigenous microbial community development.

The available information on the water quality performance of pervious surfaces and structures demonstrates that they are capable of retaining pollutants that are sediment-associated and capable of being filtered or deposited; or those which are adsorbed on to the construction materials. Where such structures are open-textured and internally well-aerated, bio-degradation processes also reduce the levels of organic materials in the runoff.

Although there is some doubt about the fate of dissolved pollutants, the water quality from pervious surfaces is unlikely to be worse than that from conventional surfaces. The infiltration of effluent in locations where groundwater could become contaminated must be carefully reviewed. It is advisable to underseal pervious surfaces where the potential for harm exists and to provide the opportunity for monitoring and prevention of discharge, where required.

A7   Adoption and legislation

The issues of adoption, ownership and responsibility of sustainable drainage systems are high on the political agenda and the national SUDS working parties (led by the Environment Agency and SEPA) are working to resolve this issue. At present the issues are resolved on a site by site basis.

The England National SUDS Working Party includes representatives from:

- Department for Transport, Local Government and the Regions
- Department for Environment, Food and Rural Affairs
- National Assembly for Wales
- Office of Water Services
- water industry
- Local Government Association
- Environment Agency
- Association of Highway Authorities
- House Builders Federation
- Association of British Insurers.

The working party is developing a framework that will provide a set of core standards and agreements between those public organisations with statutory or regulatory responsibilities relating to SUDS, including ownership and maintenance responsibilities.

There are several options relating to the responsibility for maintenance:

- local authorities become wholly responsible
- sewerage undertakers become wholly responsible
- Environment Agency becomes wholly responsible
- Scottish framework example (Box A7.1).

Box A7.1   *Current Scottish framework for maintenance responsibility*

Above-ground works, such as filter strips, swales, ponds, basins, wetlands, are maintained by the local authority.

Below-ground works, such as perforated pipes and surroundings, soakaways, filter drains, are maintained by the water authority.

The organisation with downstream responsibility will also be responsible for discharge to watercourse where applicable.

See CIRIA 2001(a) for further details.

Other legal issues that are being resolved include:

- regulatory body finalisation of policy to support sewerage undertakers' adoption of SUDS
- governing bodies allocated power to fund adoption and maintenance of SUDS in perpetuity
- governing bodies allocated power to operate as a sewerage undertaker in respect of surface water and SUDS within the existing regulatory framework

- governing bodies given duty to ensure that an organisation has agreed a maintenance regime for SUDS as part of the planning process or road scheme approval

- withdrawal of developers' automatic right of connection to sewer where SUDS is the preferred drainage system by the local authority

- requirement by land-owners to provide covenants stipulating who is responsible for maintaining unadopted SUDS on their land and that no greywater or foul drainage will be discharged to SUDS

- operating bodies to establish policies to support and promote SUDS

- requirement to establish policy in all development plans or in supplementary guidance that SUDS is to be the preferred method of surface water drainage from all new developments, as recommended in Planning Policy Guidance (PPG25) in England (see below).

The recent publication of PPG25, relating to development and flood risks, will assist in the uptake of the use of pervious pavements as a sustainable drainage technique. The guidance states that:

- the susceptibility of land to flooding is a material planning consideration

- the Environment Agency has the lead role in providing advice on flood issues at a strategic level and in relation to planning applications

- policies in development plans should outline the consideration that will be given to flood issues recognising the uncertainties that are inherent in the prediction of flooding and that flood risk is expected to increase as a result of climate change

- planning decision should apply the precautionary principle to the issue of flood risk using a risk-based search sequence to avoid such risk where possible and managing it elsewhere

- local planning authorities should work with the Environment Agency, sewerage undertakers and water companies to encourage the use of sustainable drainage

- planning policies and decisions should recognise that the consideration of flood risk and its management needs to be applied on a whole-catchment basis and not be restricted to flood plains.

The guidance promotes the use of sustainable drainage systems. Part H3 of the Building Regulations 2002 has been amended to encourage the greater use of infiltration and other sustainable drainage systems. Appendix E of the proposed document is dedicated to promoting the benefits of sustainable drainage systems.

Where pervious surfaces are part of the highway drainage system to be adopted by the Highways Authority there will be only one organisation responsible for maintenance, which should overcome many of the issues discussed above.

In Wales, the equivalent guidance on planning and flood risk will be published as Technical Advice Note 15 (TAN 15), which is undergoing consultation.